G000149504

CENTRAL HEATING
A Complete Guide

John Bowyer

DAVID & CHARLES

NEWTON ABBOT · LONDON · NORTH POMFRET (VT)
VANCOUVER

ISBN 0 7153 7037 5
Library of Congress Catalog Card Number 76-40808

© Text and Charts John Bowyer 1977

Set in 11 on 12 Mallard
and printed in Great Britain
by Biddles Limited   Guildford
for David & Charles (Publishers) Limited
Brunel House   Newton Abbot   Devon
Published in the United States of America
by David & Charles Inc
North Pomfret   Vermont 05053 USA

Published in Canada
by Douglas David & Charles Limited
North Vancouver   BC
1875 Welch Street   North Vancouver   BC

Contents

Introduction 4
1 What Is Central Heating? 7
2 Wet Systems 12
3 Boilers 25
4 Dry Systems 36
5 Running Costs 46
6 The Installation 58
7 Automatic Controls 76
8 Heat Losses 88
9 Sizing the Plant 100
10 Thermal Insulation 116
11 Buying the Installation 130
Index 143

Introduction

It has often been said that after the purchase of a house and a car, central heating is the biggest single item of expenditure a family ever has to meet. Those coming to meet this expense may well feel that they could do with some advice — advice on what they can expect for their money, on what the proposed system will do, what its disadvantages are, how much it will cost to run compared with other systems and other fuels, what is the cheapest way of paying for it, and so on.

Where are they to go for such help? If they approach one of the fuel suppliers — the gas board or the electricity board or an oil or coal merchant — they will certainly get advice, and possibly be given the name of an approved installer. But the recommendation from the gas board will be for a gas-fired system, from the electricity board for an electric one, and similarly for the other fuels. The information given, particularly in the matter of running costs, is likely to vary from the incomplete or optimistic to the simply untrue.

Should they then go to a heating installer — one independent of the various fuel interests? If they can find a well-established firm of repute who installs house heating, then any advice it can give will certainly be useful. But the staff and time that a company can devote to such purposes must be strictly limited, and such firms are not easily found; for the margin of profit in heating installation work is so small that many large heating firms do not install domestic systems at all. The enormous growth in home central heating in recent years has been met almost entirely by small plumbing firms who have become self-appointed heating engineers and who are able to provide only the sort of information that can be acquired from a study of manufacturers' catalogues.

It is to supply such advice as a would-be purchaser is likely to need, and indeed to provide information on all aspects of central heating for the home, that this book has been written. Its main objects can be summarised as follows:

(1) To enable the reader to compare the characteristics of the various systems available — heating by hot water, by warm air or by direct radiation.

(2) To enable him, or her, to compare running costs for alternative fuels for his own home, whether it be house, bungalow or flat, before committing himself to a particular fuel.

(3) To enable him to determine the output and size of heating equipment (boiler, radiators, air ducts etc) for his own house and his own needs so that he can assess quotations when he gets these from heating contractors.

(4) To set out the basic requirements of a sound heating installation to arm the reader against incompetent or unscrupulous installers.

(5) To give the facts about thermal insulation, and to show how to calculate the fuel savings that will accrue from insulating and double-glazing a building, and how to calculate the real return from money spent on such insulation.

(6) To show how to work out the real costs of alternative ways of paying for the installation, and the real total cost of one installation compared with another.

The reader may welcome a word of reassurance about what is expected of him or her. No technical knowledge is assumed, and wherever possible graphs and nomograms have been devised to do away with calculations or reduce them to a minimum. Examples are included to illustrate the use of the various tables and charts. A small amount of arithmetic remains for those who wish to get from the book all it has to offer, but this involves nothing more difficult than multiplication. An engineer would use a slide rule or pocket calculator to do the sums. A similar aid has been prepared for the reader in the form of an alignment chart for multiplication (Fig 5, p 49). A straight-edge — a ruler or the edge of a sheet of writing paper — laid across the chart performs the operation painlessly.

Technical terms have been kept to a minimum. Where they are unavoidable they are explained as they arise.

The use of imperial, that is English, units of measurement perhaps calls for a word of explanation at a time when metrication is fashionable. This is not the place to argue the case for one system or the other. But the book has been written for use and, so far as lies in the power of the author, all unnecessary difficulties have been removed. To expect the reader to work out the floor area of a room in square metres when his tape measure is marked in feet, and when nature has provided him with a pair of feet adequate for the purpose, is to introduce needless complications.

There are other reasons. The Metrication Board recommend that in engineering both the British system and the traditional Continental metric system be replaced by the new MKS (or SI) system. For heating calculations this new system (which has no unit of heat, only a general unit of energy) is far less convenient than either of the traditional systems.

Imperial units are therefore used throughout the book. However, for those who need it, a scale for the conversion of temperature from degrees Fahrenheit to degrees Celsius (centigrade), or vice versa, is included (Fig 19, p 114). On the same page there is a scale for the conversion of heater ratings in British thermal units per hour to kilowatts, or vice versa.

Chapter 1

What Is Central Heating?

So many forms of heating are nowadays referred to as 'central heating' that we should perhaps make clear what we mean by the term. We shall use it in its original sense, namely the heating of a building from a source located at some central point. A fuel-consuming source of heat within a room — an electric block storage heater for instance — will be called a room heater. This term is also applied to the heat emitters — radiators for instance — forming part of a central heating system. Although we are chiefly concerned with central heating, we shall be considering other methods of room heating, including electric ones.

In the last twenty years or so the range of central heating has often been extended to include the heating of whole districts from one central source. District heating is not dealt with in this book.

Heat and Temperature

The designer of a heating system is very much concerned with the transmission of heat from one place to another, with the rate at which it is transferred, and with the temperature differences which cause the transmission to take place. Heat transfer is of course governed by certain well-established physical laws. These the reader does not need to know. He or she may, however, find some of the explanations easier to follow if the concepts of heat and temperature are clearly distinguished from the start.

Heat is a form of energy, and temperature measures the concentration of heat. The reader may find it helpful to visualise heat as a sort of coloured dye; not a very good dye, because it always runs. Everything that exists has some of the dye in it, but in some things the concentration is higher than in others. The dye will always run from an object with a high concentration to one where the concentration is lower. It is the concentration, not the total amount of dye present, which governs how it will spread. A tiny amount of concentrated dye will seep into surroundings which may contain a larger amount of dye, but more diffusely spread.

In the same way heat will flow from small areas of high concentration (high temperature) to small or large areas of low concentration (low temperature). The rate of spread will depend on the difference of concentration in the two areas.

To continue the analogy, the heating engineer is concerned with the rate at which the dye spreads from one object to another under varying conditions. This rate must depend on the relative concentrations of dye. The relative concentrations, or temperature differences, are of basic importance in governing the rate of spread of the dye, or flow of heat.

Temperature in the imperial system is measured in degrees Fahrenheit, the temperature scale being defined by the melting point of ice (32°) and the boiling point of water (212°). It will be seen that there are 180 divisions, or degrees, between these two points. The fineness of the degrees enables us to express heating temperatures always as whole numbers, a convenience denied to users of the centigrade scale. Temperatures in Britain are always positive numbers on the Fahrenheit scale.

The unit of heat is the British thermal unit, or Btu. It is that quantity of heat which will raise the temperature of one pound weight of water by 1°F. A pound of water is one-tenth of a gallon. In terms of the coloured dye, the unit of heat might be defined as the quantity of dye needed to deepen the colour of one pound of water by one shade.

8

Before looking at the various types of heating system which are available we must establish one or two basic facts about the transfer of heat within a room, and how this influences the comfort of people in the room.

Heating a Room

Consider a room heated by an ordinary radiator. Despite the name, only a minor part of the heat output from the radiator is by radiation. The major part is by convection, that is to say by the heating of air in contact with the radiator surface.

This warmed air expands and rises, displaced by heavy cooler air from the rest of the room, air which is warmed and rises in turn. Pushed aside by the rising column, the air near the ceiling moves across the room, giving up heat to the ceiling and walls and by mixing with cooler air, and becoming less buoyant as it does so. Dropping as it cools, it finally reaches the floor, where it returns to the radiator to be warmed and to rise again. The process is a continuous one which must occur whenever any object in a room is maintained at a higher temperature than the surrounding air.

The reverse happens with a cold surface. This chills the air, causing it to drop to the floor and spread there. The combination of a cold window on one side of a room and a hot radiator on the opposite wall will produce a strong circulation of air which may be too cold for comfort at ankle level. So, where possible, radiators are installed below windows. There they counteract the window's natural down-draught, the window being the coldest surface in a room in winter.

Placing the radiator in that position also makes the best use of its radiant heat emission. That is the heat which passes directly from a hot body to a cooler one without the agency of any intervening medium such as air. The most important instance of this form of heat transmission is the heat which the earth receives from the sun. That comes entirely by radiation. Radiant heat travels, like light, in straight lines. Because of this we

9

can only receive radiant heat from a source we can see, that is to say a source which is in an unobstructed straight line from us. Transmitted as it is in straight lines, radiant heat is not affected by the relative positions of source and receiver. It is transmitted downwards or sideways as readily as upwards. The saying that 'heat rises' applies only to convection.

The human body must lose heat at all times to remain healthy; it is a normal part of the life process. When we feel cold it is because the rate of loss is too high. In a comfortably heated room the temperature of the body, even of the clothing surface, is higher than that of the room air, so the body gives up heat by convection to the air. It also gives up heat by direct radiation to surfaces cooler than itself in the room. That includes floor, walls, window, ceiling — everything except the radiator which we are considering as the room's source of heat. The radiator is the only surface in the room warmer than the human occupants. By placing the radiator beneath the window we can offset the radiation heat loss to the window of the people in the room. A human body which can 'see' the cold window — that is, is not shielded by some interposed object — can also 'see' the hot radiator. The effect on the occupants is to even out the variations in room surface temperature and thereby to produce a greater sensation of comfort.

The average of all the surface temperatures of a room, taking into acccount the areas and positions of the various surfaces, is known as the mean radiant temperature (MRT) of the room. Two rooms of similar shape but with different MRTs will need different room air temperatures to produce similar sensations of comfort. The room with the higher MRT will be comfortable at a lower air temperature.

This fact is of importance because the rate of heat consumption in any room depends very largely on the level of the room air temperature, this being the temperature measured with an ordinary thermometer. Clearly, if we can achieve the required level of comfort with a lower air temperature than usual we can make fuel savings. We can do so if we can increase the MRT of the room, either by using a high temperature heat source close to the room occupants, or by extending the heat source over a sizeable area of the room surface.

Under the first alternative — the use of high temperature heaters — both gas and electric fires, not to mention ordinary coal fires, are very common. They provide room heating, not central heating, but some can be used in conjunction with central heating systems (see Chapter 3). The second method of raising the MRT — by extending the heat source — is not so common. It is known as 'panel heating', and it uses the floor or ceiling of the room as a comparatively low temperature (75° to 100°F) source of heat, thereby spreading the emitting surface over as large an area as possible.

Because they raise the room MRT, panel systems are classified as radiant heating, though a significant part of the heat output from them is in fact by convection. They have other advantages over purely convective systems. The air temperature variation from floor to ceiling is small in a radiantly heated room; this in itself is conducive to comfort. The small temperature gradient is also desirable for the sake of fuel economy, particularly in a high room, as the heat loss from the room, which depends on the indoor-outdoor temperature difference, is greater when warm air accumulates near the ceiling.

In examining the various kinds of heating apparatus we shall find that some are entirely convective and some partly radiative and partly convective. A completely radiant room heater is not feasible, of course, as any warm surface in a room must heat the air in contact with it, and some convection is bound to ensue.

Natural convection, the only kind so far considered, is caused by the difference in density of hot and cold air. Forced convection is the name given to the process which uses a fan to blow air over a hot surface to pick up heat. A heating surface designed for convection of either sort is usually finned like a car radiator to improve the rate of heat transfer.

Chapter 2

Wet Systems

Pipe Materials

Wet systems are those using water as a heat carrying medium. They grew directly from the use of a boiler to heat water for household purposes — for baths, washing, cleaning and washing-up. This is still one of the functions of the heating boiler, though in a combined heating and hot water system the domestic hot water no longer passes through the boiler itself but through a heat exchanger which is in turn heated by the boiler.

This indirect method of heating the domestic water is adopted to minimise pipe and boiler corrosion. Mains water is alkaline or acidic (hard or soft), and contains varying amounts of dissolved gases and chemical salts. Its tendency to fur up pipes or to attack metal and cause corrosion depends on these characteristics, the tendency increasing with the water temperature. Water for household purposes is heated, used and replaced by fresh cold water many times a day, so there is a constant change of water in the system. The factors which cause corrosion are renewed each time fresh water enters from the mains. Untreated steel pipes would very soon be eaten away under these circumstances, so where steel is used in a water supply system it is specially treated to resist attack by being galvanised (zinc coated) during manufacture. Where the water supply is acidic, galvanised pipes are not suitable however, and copper — which is more expensive — must be used.

The same restriction does not apply to the space heating system. There the water is changed so infrequently — perhaps once a year — that untreated steel pipes may be used with impunity. In recent years, however, the diameter of the pipes used in heating systems has been reduced so much that there is no longer the same economic incentive to use steel. The making of pipe joints is simpler and quicker with copper, so the reduced labour cost in pipe jointing may more than offset the additional cost of the copper pipes. With the so-called 'microbore' systems, where the pipes are ¼ in in diameter with virtually no joints, copper is universally used.

It may be asked why small bore pipes cannot be used with the domestic hot water supply system, thereby reducing its cost. The answer is that the outflow of water from the taps, which depends on the pressure head of the water standing in the system, would be too slow with pipes smaller than those normally used.

Components of the System

A wet heating system contains a boiler, a range of pipework, room heaters of some kind, a feed tank and, nowadays, a circulating pump. The system can be designed to circulate by natural convection of the water in it (gravity circulation) without a pump, but the pipes are then large. Modern pumps are reliable and comparatively cheap, so there is no reason to do without them. The domestic hot water half of the system contains pipes and a storage cylinder.

There seems occasionally to be some confusion about the terms boiler and hot water cylinder, so it may be pointed out here that the boiler is where the fuel is burned and the cylinder is where domestic hot water is stored. The cylinder is often in an airing cupboard. Domestic hot water service is often abbreviated to HWS.

13

The boiler is of course the primary source of heat for the whole system, including the HWS. However, in order to keep the two parts of the system separate — for the reasons already given — the domestic hot water has its own secondary source of heat. This is a coil of pipe, or the equivalent, fitted inside the storage cylinder and fed from the boiler. The constantly changing domestic water cannot then pass through the boiler or heating pipes. A storage cylinder with its own heating element of this kind is called an indirect cylinder. The heating element raises the contents of the cylinder from cold to the desired storage temperature.

Instead of the arrangement described, the domestic hot water may be heated by some independent means such as an electric immersion heater. In large installations a special HWS boiler may even be put in. This type of boiler is treated internally to resist corrosion. Such a hot water system is completely independent of the heating system. However, for most house installations the boiler is chosen with sufficient output to cope with both the space heating and the HWS. To save running the boiler in summer an immersion heater is often fitted in the indirect cylinder.

A combined radiator heating and HWS system is shown in Fig 1. The hottest water in the boiler is at the top, so the flow pipes to both the heating and HWS circuits are taken from the top of the boiler and the return pipes connected to the bottom. Temperatures at the boiler are typically 180°F flow and 160° return. The direction of water circulation is indicated by arrows. Though it continues through the boiler, the speed of flow there is so much less than in the pipes that we may consider the boiler to be a sort of tank with uniform pressure conditions throughout.

The circulation through the heating system is produced by the pump. There is no pump in the pipes from the boiler to the hot water cylinder. There the circulation is by natural gravity, that is to say convection brought about by the difference in density of hot water in the flow pipe and cooler water in the return. The pressure difference producing such circulation is always very small and easily overcome. Only because of the 'tank' effect mentioned above does the heating pump not interfere with the HWS circulation. If the cylinder connections were made to the heating flow and return pipes rather than directly to the boiler, the effect of the pump could no longer be ignored. It might stop or reverse the flow to the cylinder.

Some installations are designed to operate with a pumped circulation to the cylinder as well as to the heating system. In such a case the cylinder connections are taken from the heating flow and return pipes, with the pump between them. But the arrangement shown in Fig 1 has certain advantages which will be considered later. For the moment we merely point out that with it the heating of the domestic hot water is not dependent on the operation of the pump.

The heating feed tank is a small open-topped tank at the highest point of the heating system. It is usually installed in the loft, near the main cold water storage tank. It has two functions. It forms a break between the public water main and the house heating system, to protect the water main from pollution, and it absorbs

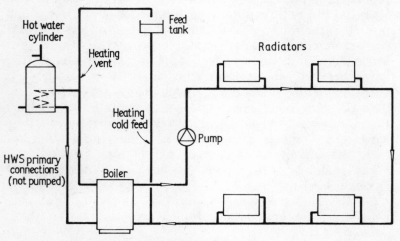

Fig 1   Single pipe heating system

15

the expansion of the water in the system when heated. If there were no tank, water would have to be expelled from the system by some means on heating, and fresh water drawn in on cooling. Quite apart from the difficulty of arranging this, such regular water change would promote corrosion. The feed and expansion tank is a simple device to meet both requirements.

The heating cold feed pipe is used for filling the system initially and, thereafter, as the connection between the tank and the system, to allow the expansion and contraction of the water with temperature change. Because of this it becomes hot in use, despite its name.

The heating and HWS vent pipes allow air to escape from the system while it is being filled, and provide a third line of defence against the remote possibility of excess pressure. The two other pressure relief devices are the cold feed pipe and the boiler safety valve. Although the vent pipes are turned over the heating and cold water tanks, they should not in normal use discharge any water.

The heating pump — sometimes, for no good reason, called an accelerator — circulates water through the system against the resistance to flow offered by the pipes, the pipe fittings and the heating apparatus. It can be fitted in the flow pipe from the boiler or in the return pipe to the boiler. The choice of position has certain consequences which are considered in Chapter 6, but these do not affect the pump's function of circulating water round the system. The head of a pump is a measure of the pressure it develops. Expressed in feet, it is the height to which the pump would raise water through perfectly smooth pipes with no friction or other losses. In a closed circuit such as a heating system the head is entirely used in overcoming pipe friction and other resistances to flow. The rate of water delivery varies with the head. By increasing the resistance against which the pump is working, by partially closing a valve for instance, the rate of water flow is reduced.

Single Pipe System

The heating system shown in Fig 1 is known as a single pipe system because a single pipe carries the water to and from each radiator in turn. A particular installation may be divided into more than one branch, but if the radiator flow and return connections are always both taken from a common pipe, the system is a single pipe one. It has the virtue of simplicity and is neat in appearance.

As the water from each radiator is returned into the single main, the water fed to the last radiator is cooler than that fed to the first. For a given output of heat, therefore, a radiator at the end of the circuit has to be larger than one near the beginning.

The pressure difference across the radiator which causes the flow of water through it comes chiefly from the friction of the water in the main pipe beneath the radiator. For the short distance between the radiator connections this is not very great, so heaters other than radiators, having a higher resistance to water flow, are not suitable for use with a single pipe system.

Two-pipe System

The alternative is the two-pipe system, shown in Fig 2. The diagram shows an installation with two branches, one serving the ground floor and one the first, but there may be only one branch or any other number.

With this piping arrangement each radiator or other heater is connected across a pair of flow and return mains. The circulating pressure through each radiator is higher than with the single pipe system, being equal to the head of the heating pump less the pressure lost in pipe friction to and from the radiator in question.

All the heaters receive water at almost boiler flow temperature. Although there is some drop in water temperature between the radiators nearer to the boiler and those more distant from it, this is offset by proportioning the rate of flow to each heater to maintain

17

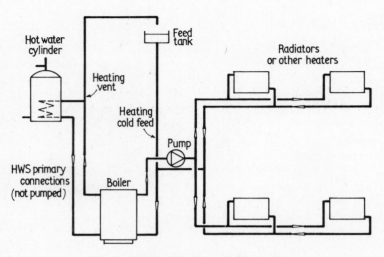

Fig 2   Two-pipe heating system

a constant mean temperature throughout the system. All heaters of a given output are therefore of the same size.

The two-pipe system is not so neat in appearance as the single pipe and it uses more tube. It is the only one that can be used with convectors (of all types) and with microbore piping.

Microbore systems now usually incorporate a distribution manifold. This is a distribution box located at some convenient central point — often between floor joists on the first floor — from which the very small bore pipes are run to each heater or room. The manifold is fed with flow and return mains of larger bore from the boiler. This is probably the cheapest wet system available. The pump in any installation using such small bore pipes must be specially selected for the high head needed.

Pressurised Systems

The pressure to which water is subjected governs the temperature at which it will boil. At sea level water boils at 212°F. On a mountain it will boil at a lower

18

temperature. Down in a mine it boils at a higher temperature; it has to be heated above 212° before it will start to form steam.

Use is made of this fact in pressurised systems. If all the water in a heating installation can be pressurised the water can be raised in temperature to 220°, 250° or 300° or more — depending on the pressure — without changing to steam. This high temperature water can be cooled inside the heating apparatus through a wide temperature range, giving up a correspondingly large amount of heat.

Pressurised water systems have been used in industrial heating for many years in place of steam. One version has been available for small installations for just as long, but has not been widely used. Recently there have been attempts to promote the use of pressurised systems in the domestic market. In the author's opinion these attempts are misguided. There are cogent economic arguments for a pressurised water system instead of a steam system in a factory, but they do not apply to a house heating installation, where the alternatives are the other wet systems we have already considered.

Where pressurised systems are used domestically the temperatures do not normally exceed 230°F. Precautions must be taken against the possibility of contact with any surface at temperatures over 190°F if burning is to be avoided.

The Domestic Hot Water System

With any of the heating systems considered the primary circulation to the HWS cylinder may be either pumped or by gravity circulation. The arrangement of the secondary side of the HWS system — that is to say the water delivered to the taps — is as shown in Fig 3. The secondary side is completely unaffected by the method of primary circulation used.

The outflow from a tap is caused by the head of water in the system above the level of the tap. The head is therefore the distance between the level of water in the

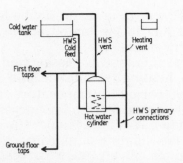

Fig 3   Domestic hot water system

cold water storage tank and the tap in question. This is obviously much less for first floor taps than for those on the ground floor.

If a shower bath is installed, with a hot and cold water mixing valve, the head available on the first floor may not be sufficient to provide the required outflow of water against the combined resistances of the mixing valve and shower head fitting. This point should always be checked with the installer — or, better, with the mixing valve manufacturer — before the shower is installed. If the shower can be fitted on the ground floor no problem should arise, except possibly in a bungalow. When checking such points it must be remembered that the head causing flow is that between the free water level in the cold water storage tank and the shower *outlet*, not the mixing valve. Allowance should be made by the installer for friction in the remainder of the pipework, and the pipe sized accordingly.

Radiators

Radiators are so well known that a description is hardly needed. They are available in three basic shapes: column, hospital or panel. Column radiators are made of cast iron. Hospital radiators can be of cast iron or pressed steel. Panel radiators are almost always of pressed steel. These last are by far the most commonly used type for domestic heating. They have one, two, or

20

even three panels, separated by air spaces. Three-panel models are rather clumsy in appearance and seldom used.

The proportions of heat emitted by radiation and convection vary with the number of panels. Allowing for the fact that radiation from the back of the heater to the wall behind only reaches the room after being converted into convected warm air, the effective proportions of heat emitted under each heading are:

Single panel	70% convection	30% radiation
Double panel	80% convection	20% radiation
Triple panel	85% convection	15% radiation

Radiators are simple, cheap and effective. Steel radiators are more subject to corrosion than cast iron ones, and they are more easily damaged by it, owing to the thinness of the sheet metal walls. All types can be used in single or two-pipe systems. If installed as usual below windows, care should be taken that the emission is not shielded or deflected to the window when curtains are drawn.

Natural Convectors

These are slim metal boxes with an opening near the top and a finned tubular heating element fitted inside at the bottom. They stand a few inches clear of the floor, supported on feet or fastened to the wall. The column of warm air inside the casing produces a draught as with a chimney, drawing a continual supply of air from the room into the bottom of the heater to replace that discharged through the grille at the top. An air damper to control the output is fitted internally and can be operated by a knob on the front of the casing.

Convectors are smaller than radiators for a given output of heat, but usually deeper from front to back. The copper heating element combines well with a copper pipe installation. Corrosion, always aggravated by a mixture of metals, is non-existent. Convectors

21

cannot be used in single pipe systems. They can be concealed within a false wall or recess so long as an air inlet opening is provided. As the name implies, their heat output is entirely convective.

Fan Convectors

These have finned tubular heating elements, as with natural convectors, but the air is blown through them by an electric fan. They have much greater heat outputs than natural convectors and are used in areas such as halls and stairways where their larger bulk is not a handicap and where their quick response to load changes — an open front door for instance — can be used to the full. The fan motor is usually controlled by a thermostat, either fitted in the air inlet at the bottom of the casing or installed on one wall of the heated space. Fan convectors cannot be used in single pipe systems, but pumped two-pipe connections can often be provided for an isolated heater from what is otherwise a single pipe system. The heat output is entirely convective.

Skirting Heaters

These are continuous natural convectors run round the room at skirting level. They replace the normal skirting board, being about 8in high and projecting 2in from the wall. They are fitted clear of the floor to allow air entry at the bottom. Dummy lengths, without heating elements, are used to make up the remainder of the skirting beyond that needed to heat the room. Hand operated internal control dampers are sometimes fitted to the heated lengths.

The original version of these heaters was of cast iron. Those most commonly used today are pressed from sheet steel. Where there is the possibility of damage from children or from frequent moving of furniture the sheet steel variety is not, in the author's opinion, really suitable for domestic use.

Depending on the type, the output can be partly

radiative or entirely convective. The heat emission is at a low level over an extended length, so the tendency to large temperature gradients inherent in convective heating is reduced. Skirting heaters can be used in single pipe or two-pipe systems.

A development from these heaters, used in offices but very little in private houses, is the continuous convector ('sill-line' heater) which runs across one wall of a room with the outlet at window sill level.

Unit Heaters

Unit heaters are designed for industrial heating and are not suitable for installation in a house. They are useful for heating a garage or workshop, assuming of course the building is within a convenient distance of the house heating mains. The units are suspended at high level in the space to be heated. They contain a finned tube heater battery through which air is blown by an electric fan, on the same principle as a fan convector. Adjustable louvres direct the warm air downwards. The units can be controlled automatically by a room thermostat which switches the fan. They need pumped two-pipe connections. As with fan convectors, these are usually not difficult to provide for a single unit whatever the general system may be. The heat output is entirely convective.

Panel Heating

The forms of heating so far considered can be installed equally well in a new or an existing house. Panel heating, by pipe coils embedded in the floor, ceiling or (rarely) walls of a building, can only be installed while the house is being built. The design and installation of a panel system is specialist work and should only be entrusted to those experienced in it. Heating contractors who carry out this work are usually members of the Invisible Panel Warming Association.

The water temperatures used for panel heating are

much lower than for radiator or convector systems — usually in the region of 110°F. It is better to run the boiler at a higher temperature than this, both to provide heat to the HWS cylinder and also because heating boilers are designed to work most efficiently at temperatures approaching 200°F. An arrangement is usually made to permit the boiler to operate at the higher temperature while providing much cooler water for the panel heating coils (see for instance Fig 11, p 82).

The system is expensive to install, chiefly because it has to be dovetailed into the builder's construction programme. The decision to use panel heating must be made at the architect's sketch plan stage as he must provide a floor or ceiling structure suitable for it. A drawback of the floor and wall versions is that because of the mass of material heated, the system responds fairly slowly to load changes.

Against these disadvantages must be set the fact that the heating installation is completely invisible and takes up no room space. Temperature gradients in the rooms are very small, leading to fuel economy. The large expanse of heated surface — virtually the whole of the floor or ceiling — produces a high mean radiant temperature in the room, and comfort is achieved at lower room temperatures than would otherwise be acceptable. This again leads to fuel economy.

The proportions of convective and radiant heat emission with the floor, wall and ceiling surface temperatures commonly used are as follows:

Floor panel   45% convection   55% radiation
Wall panel   43% convection   57% radiation
Ceiling panel   30% convection   70% radiation

The proportions for the ceiling panel vary with the size of panel and with the spacing of the pipe coils. Convection here is caused by differential temperatures across the face of the ceiling and by stray air currents in the room.

Chapter 3
Boilers

The heat source of a wet system is of course the boiler. Despite its name it should not boil the water. It heats the water to a temperature governed by the setting of its control thermostat. In winter this is usually 180°F. The temperature can be higher, but then there is a risk of injury from hot pipes and radiators.

The modern heating boiler is designed for use with a specific fuel — coal, gas or oil. The combustion requirements and the heat exchange characteristics of solid fuel are different from those of gas or oil, so a conversion from one fuel to another is seldom satisfactory. There is, however, at least one make of boiler now available which is specially designed to be readily converted from oil to gas burning, or vice versa. It is more expensive than single fuel boilers of comparable output. The manufacturers claim that, as future fuel prices are unpredictable, a convertible boiler is the best choice.

The running costs for the various fuels will be dealt with in Chapter 5, but the choice of fuel may be partly governed by other considerations such as the cost of the plant to install, the space taken up by the boiler or fuel, convenience in use and so on. These aspects will be considered here.

Solid fuel boilers burn coal, coke or other processed fuels derived from coal. The makers' recommendations on suitable grades of fuel should always be followed. The boiler can be either a small unit of limited output, combined with a room heater, or a central unit of any output whatever.

Back Boilers

Originally developed to provide domestic hot water from the living room fire, the design has changed over the years to include larger heat transfer surfaces and in some models a forced draught fan, permitting a much higher combustion efficiency. This has been achieved at the cost of enclosing the front of the fire with glass doors. The larger models have a total output exceeding 40,000Btu per hour, more than three-quarters of which goes into the back boiler, the remainder being radiated and convected from the fire directly to the room where the appliance is installed. A boiler of 30,000Btu per hour capacity can cope with several radiators as well as the domestic hot water.

A thermostat is included to control the water temperature. There is usually a damper control to permit the boiler output to be increased without greatly increasing the heat emitted from the front of the fire to the room. An economiser can be added to some models. This is fitted in the chimney immediately above the boiler, to which it is interconnected. The extra heating surface thus provided increases the boiler rating by about 5,000Btu per hour.

Where the total heating load is within the capacity of these room-heater/boilers, they have the assets of cheapness and simplicity and the attraction of an open fire — albeit behind glass. They have to be stoked by hand, of course, and ashes and clinker must be removed regularly.

Other Solid Fuel Boilers

Solid fuel boilers of more conventional type are available in any size, from the small hot water boiler with an output of under 20,000Btu per hour, once found in almost every kitchen, to industrial boilers with automatic stokers and a rating of perhaps 20 million Btu per hour. The range of sizes in which we are interested is from about 30,000 to 150,000Btu per hour. A typical boiler rating for a three-bedroomed detached house would be 60,000Btu per hour, including the domestic hot water service. Boilers in this range can be either hand-fired from the front, or of magazine type with a built-in fuel hopper.

Hand-fired boilers need to be stoked during the day, and to have ashes and clinker removed once a day. There is a built-in thermostat which operates a damper to control the rate of burning. They are cheap to install and simple in operation, so there is little to go wrong. They are clean and smart in appearance, having a stove enamelled casing, and can be installed in a kitchen, though, because of the stoking and ash removal, some people prefer to put them in an outhouse or scullery.

Magazine boilers incorporate a fuel hopper which needs to be filled about once a day in winter and once every four or five days in summer. The fuel falls under its own weight into the combustion chamber to keep the fire topped up. One popular make has a declinkering lever fitted to the side of the boiler. This is used to jettison the ash and clinker into the ash tray, which has to be emptied once or twice a week. There is a built-in forced draught fan which is under the control of the boiler thermostat. The fan ensures a quick response to load changes and enables hard coke or anthracite to be used, with a consequent economy in running costs.

It will be seen that magazine boilers are more sophisticated appliances than hand-fired boilers, and they are more expensive. They are similar in appearance, though because of the internal fuel hopper they are more bulky than a hand-fired boiler of similar output. They can be installed in the kitchen.

All solid fuel boilers have the advantage of using a home-produced fuel. They all, to a varying extent, demand the tasks of stoking and ash removal. Fuel storage space is needed — about 15sq ft of floor area for the average house.

Oil Fired Boilers

There are three kinds of oil burner used with domestic heating boilers: vaporising, wallflame and pressure jet.

Vaporising burners appear in a number of forms, the simpler varieties having an oil reservoir and being manually lit and operated. These are now largely superseded by automatically operated units, with electric ignition and in many cases with the combustion air supplied by an electric fan. In these the oil supply to the burner is metered automatically and the burner alternates between full output and off, under the control of the boiler water flow thermostat.

The wallflame burner is a development from the fan assisted vaporising burner. It contains a centrifugal rotor which throws the oil outwards on to a circular containing wall where the oil vaporises and burns. These burners also are fully automatic in operation, under the control of the boiler thermostat.

The action of the pressure jet burner in different from that of the others. In it oil is pumped under pressure to a nozzle, from which it emerges as a fine spray. The air for combustion is blown into the boiler through a tube which surrounds the nozzle, and the air/fuel mixture is ignited by an electric spark across a pair of high voltage electrodes in the path of the mixture. Once alight, the flame becomes self-supporting and the electric current is automatically switched off. These burners also are fully automatic in operation under the control of the boiler thermostat.

Both the vaporising and wallflame burners use kerosene oil of 28sec viscosity. Viscosity is a measure of the stickiness of the oil, 28sec being the time taken for a specified amount to run through a standard sized aperture. Compared with these, the pressure jet burner uses a slightly cheaper and heavier grade of oil — of 35sec viscosity. The pressure jet burner is also a little more efficient, which is to say it gets more heat out of each gallon of oil burned. The chief drawback of the pressure jet is its noise.

Because of this it is not possible to install a pressure jet boiler in any living area, including the kitchen. It must be sited in an outhouse. Even then care should be taken with the chimney so that noise is not transmitted through it to bedrooms or other quiet areas. Some ingenuity has been shown by manufacturers in attempts to reduce the noise from these burners. The best advice that can be offered to a prospective purchaser, if he has been assured that some particular boiler fitted with a pressure jet is satisfactory in a kitchen, is to insist on hearing one of the units in operation before committing himself.

An oil fired installation has to have an oil storage tank, and space must be found out of doors for this. It is usual to store enough oil for several weeks' running at full load. However, if deliveries are taken in 500gal lots the oil is reduced in price, so a storage tank of 600gal capacity (allowing some reserve while awaiting delivery) is commonly used. Some typical tank sizes are:

225gal	4ft × 3ft × 3ft	
250gal	5ft × 2ft × 4ft	
300gal	6ft × 2ft × 4ft	
600gal	6ft × 4ft × 4ft	

The oil filling pipe is connected to the top of the tank. If the tank is some distance from the nearest roadway then the fill line must be extended to a position within 100ft of the road so that the oil delivery tanker can reach it with the standard length hose.

Details of the necessary ancillary equipment and precautions against fire and explosion are given in Chapter 6.

Gas Fired Boilers

All gas fired boilers now sold are suitable for burning natural gas or, if fitted with burners for coal gas, are designed to be easily converted. Natural gas, piped from naturally occurring underground reservoirs, is largely methane. Coal gas, derived from coal by a coking process, is a mixture of hydrogen, methane and carbon monoxide. The calorific value of natural gas is about double that of coal gas, each cubic foot giving out about 1,000Btu when burned completely. The consumer pays on a heat content basis, so gains no financial advantage from a conversion to natural gas. The 'landed' cost of natural gas is so low that it is difficult to see why the price is not reduced when a conversion from coal gas is made.

There are available a number of combined gas boiler/room heaters. They are suitable for installation in existing fire places, being the equivalent of the solid fuel boiler/room heaters considered earlier. The output is a little higher, at about 40,000Btu per hour from the boiler and 10,000 from the radiant fire.

Independent gas boilers for installation in a boiler room or kitchen are similar in appearance to solid fuel or oil fired boilers. Some are lit by hand, but they are invariably fully automatic in operation and are supplied complete with thermostats and flame failure safety controls.

As a fuel, gas has the advantage of requiring no storage space at all — though circumstances can be envisaged when this total reliance on a piped supply could be a drawback. The gas boiler is clean and quiet in operation and, as with oil, there is no stoking and ash removal. The cost of gas and oil boilers are about equal — higher than that of the solid fuel boiler. In the past gas as a fuel has usually been more expensive than either coal or oil, but at the time of writing the future costs of all three are unpredictable. Chapter 5 on fuel costs will enable the reader to make his own comparisons, using whatever prices are current.

Chimneys

The functions of a boiler chimney are:
(1) To carry away smoke and flue gases at a height which will cause no inconvenience.

30

(2) To create a draught (suction) at the boiler to draw the air needed for combustion through the resistances offered by the air inlet opening, the grate, the fuel on the grate and the boiler flues.

(3) To produce enough draught to swamp the effects of fluctuating wind pressure around the building.

If these requirements can be met by some other means then a conventional chimney is not needed. Balanced flues, originally for gas boilers but now also fitted to some oil fired ones, offer such an alternative. They do it as follows.

Requirement number one is not so much met as discounted. The flue gases from gas and domestic oil fired boilers are considered sufficiently innocuous to be discharged at low level provided (Building Regulations 1965) that the outlet is not on to a public right of way and that it is at least 2ft (or 3ft for an oil boiler) away from any opening into the building. Air must be able to circulate freely about the discharge point.

The second requirement is met by reducing the resistance to air flow through the boiler and/or by using electric fans to help.

The third requirement is met by discharging the flue gases as close as possible to the point where air for combustion is drawn in. This is frequently done by using a common, but divided, duct for the incoming air and outgoing flue gases. Wind pressure variations then have a similar effect on both the air entry and the flue discharge, thereby cancelling themselves out. It is this last characteristic which has given the balanced flue its name.

Structurally a balanced flue boiler needs one hole — sometimes two — through the wall against which the boiler stands. The air and flue gas ducts pass from the back of the boiler through the wall to the terminal fitting on the outside. No chimney is needed. Inside the house the boiler is best positioned against an outside wall, for long runs of flue ducting are not possible. Any special local authority requirements must be complied with, of course, as well as the Building Regulations quoted earlier.

Since a balanced flue boiler draws its air direct from outside, the combustion chamber can be sealed off from the room in which the boiler stands. One advantage of this is that air for combustion is not drawn through the room, and this cause of draughts is eliminated.

A solid fuel boiler must be connected to a conventional chimney of some kind. If this is a recently built brick chimney, lined internally against condensation, then no modifications to it will be necessary. If it was built before 1965, however, the Building Regulations require that it be lined throughout its length to prevent condensation from the flue gases from spreading into the building structure. The regulations apply also to oil burning and gas burning equipment with conventional chimneys. Flue lining is not such a formidable task as it may sound. There are standard kits for the purpose. The lining used is a flexible tube, made of spirally wound stainless steel ribbon, which is suspended from a top clamp plate fastened to the chimney brickwork.

If there is no existing chimney, or if what there is is too small, then an asbestos chimney can be installed. This is fitted outside the boiler room and is run up to well above the eaves of the house. In the case of a gas boiler flue it must terminate with a cowl as a protection against wind and downdraughts. A plug should be included at the bottom for draining off condensation.

The connection between the boiler smoke outlet and the brick or asbestos chimney is the smoke pipe. For a gas boiler the smoke pipe should include a draught diverter (a specially designed break in the pipe) to guard the burner and pilot light against downdraughts. A draught diverter is not needed with a balanced flue boiler.

The smoke pipe from an oil fired boiler is normally fitted with a draught stabiliser. This is a hinged flap, with a counterweight, which opens to allow air into the chimney if a high flue gas temperature or a gusting wind should cause excessive suction. The stabiliser also incorporates a door, hinged to open outwards, to relieve the pressure of any explosion inside the boiler or

32

chimney. With large boilers the stabiliser is usually fitted at the base of the chimney instead of in the smoke pipe. It often does double duty as a soot door. Soot doors should be fitted at all points in a flue system where changes of direction occur. They make cleaning easier.

Fresh Air Inlets

Air is needed to burn any fuel. One gallon of oil for instance requires 2,000cu ft of air for satisfactory combustion. Provision has to be made for this. If the boiler is a balanced flue model the problem does not arise, since the air is drawn directly from outside by the boiler. For a conventional boiler Table 1 shows the minimum area of low-level ventilation opening or grille needed in the wall of the boiler room for various sizes of boiler.

Table 1
Boiler-room low-level ventilation openings

Boiler rating (Btu/h)	Minimum free area of opening (sq in)
30,000	16
40,000	22
60,000	33
80,000	44
100,000	55
150,000	80

They are free areas, that is the nett clear opening after deducting any obstructions, and they are for openings directly from outdoors. If the air inlet is from another ventilated space in the house then the figures given in the table should be doubled. A high-level grille of at least half the area of the low-level opening should also be provided to ensure adequate through ventilation.

Boiler Bases

Statutory requirements for boiler bases are set out in

33

the Building Regulations 1965, with later amendments. For boilers with outputs up to 150,000Btu per hour — and that includes virtually all domestic heating boilers — the requirements vary with the nature of the floor structure. But the effect is usually that solid fuel and oil fired boilers must stand on a plinth at least 2in high, whereas gas boilers need not. There may also be local authority by-laws on this subject, as with flues and chimneys. If so, heating contractors in the locality will know of them.

Electric Water Heaters

There are two standard types available for domestic heating. Both use off-peak electricity with thermal storage, and both are intended for use with a conventional small-bore hot water heating system.

The first uses water as the thermal storage medium. A storage tank of water, fitted with electric immersion heaters, is heated overnight to a temperature of about 200°F. (If a pressurised system is used the storage temperature can be higher, with a corresponding reduction in tank size.) The tank is well insulated to reduce heat loss. During the following day water is circulated from the tank through the heating system and back to the tank (see Fig 4).

The flow pipe is taken from the top of the tank and the return is to the bottom. There is a bypass mixing connection which dilutes the high temperature flow with some of the lower temperature water returned from the heating system. This mixing operation is controlled by a thermostat which can be either pre-set to give a fixed delivery temperature to the radiators, or can itself be controlled by an outdoor thermostat to adjust the flow temperature to the radiators in accordance with the outdoor temperature. The storage tank is sized to hold enough heat for a day under design weather conditions. If a midday electricity boost is available the tank can be smaller.

In the alternative system the thermal storage medium

34

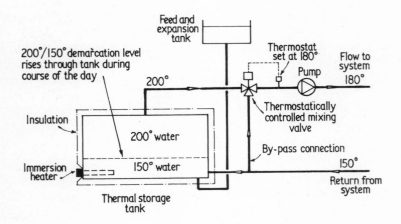

Fig 4 Water thermal storage system The contents of the
tank are heated overnight from a temperature of 150°
to 200°F. Circulation through the heating system
during the day reduces the temperature to 150°

is cast iron. In this respect the heater is similar to a
thermal storage air heater (see Chapter 4). A central
core of cast-iron blocks is heated overnight by current
at the off-peak rate. A fan circulates air through the
core to pick up heat. However, instead of blowing the
air directly to the rooms to be heated, as in the warm
air system, the fan sends the heated air through an
air-water heat exchanger to provide hot water for a
conventional wet system.

Either of the heaters described can incorporate an
additional immersion heater to act as a booster for very
cold weather. This should be fitted in or near the flow
connection. The current for the booster must of course
be paid for at normal tariff rates.

The advantages of electric water heating are cleanli-
ness, no fuel storage, no chimney and no combustion air
requirement. The disadvantage is usually the cost of the
fuel. See Chapter 5 for comparative fuel costs.

Chapter 4

Dry Systems

Dry systems are any which do not use water as a heating medium. Because of this the heating of domestic hot water has to be treated separately from the space heating. Gas or electric water heaters are commonly used, the choice usually governed by the fuel selected for space heating. Some central warm air heaters have built-in water heaters for this purpose. The unit then contains two burners or, in the case of electric heaters, two sets of heating elements — one for each service. The HWS system is usually direct (the cylinder containing no heating coil), but is otherwise no different from the typical system dealt with in Chapter 2. In this chapter, therefore, we confine our attention to space heating.

Warm Air Heating

Some forms of heating can only be installed during the construction of a building. Panel heating is one of these. Certain others, now available for any house, new or existing, were originally developed for installation at the building construction stage, and really need to be designed into the building for their assets to be fully exploited. Warm air heating, the only dry central heating system, is in this category. The air heater should be allocated a central position in the house, so that outgoing duct-runs are short and returned air can be drawn into the heater equally from all parts of the house. If this cannot be done, the chief virtue of the system — its compactness — is lost. Unless a house is designed with this sort of heater in mind such a central position will seldom be available.

Warm air systems may be fuelled by gas, oil or electricity. The burner for gas or oil fired versions is similar to that used in the corresponding boiler, and has similar needs in the way of air inlet to the heating chamber, balanced draught or conventional flue to atmosphere, safety controls and the rest. These were dealt with in Chapter 3. Electric air heaters have no flue, of course, and need no fresh air inlet.

All warm air systems work on the same general lines. Air is collected from some central point in the house, is filtered, heated and redistributed through sheet metal ducts to the various rooms. The central warm air unit contains the air filter, heater battery and fan, together with the burner or electric heating elements and the controls. Some units, including all the electric off-peak storage types, include a bypass arrangement, sending only part of the air through the heating elements and tempering this with unheated air before delivering it.

In a house designed for the system, the air ducts are concealed within the building structure. In an existing house complete concealment is seldom possible, though a good deal can be achieved by using cupboards, attic space and the space between floor joists. The duct to each room terminates at the wall, ceiling or floor surface with a 'register', that is a grille fitted with a hand- or foot-operated damper to control the air flow. Return air grilles are not usually fitted with dampers.

Most electric air heaters are designed to be charged overnight, so taking advantage of the cheaper off-peak tariff. Some have an additional provision for charging during the day to augment the overnight charge during cold weather. The heat storage core is made of refractory (furnace) brickwork, sometimes with additional cast-iron blocks. The electric heating elements are embedded in the refractory blocks, which are assembled to allow the passage of air to pick up heat from the core.

There are electric warm air systems without thermal

storage cores. The heaters are much lighter and less bulky than thermal storage models. They use electricity as and when it is needed to satisfy the heating needs of the house. This means that a great deal, if not all, of the current consumed must be paid for at normal tariff rates. Unless there is some special reason for a central system there would seem to be little point in putting in heating of this sort, which must cost no less to run and which can achieve no more in the way of comfort than any of the direct electric room heaters which are available.

All central warm air systems, whatever the fuel, are entirely convective in their heat output. Because of the high temperature of the heat source they can, particularly in cold weather when output is at a maximum, produce a feeling of stuffiness or dryness in the throat.

Room temperature gradients with central warm air systems tend to be large. This is partly because, to keep the size of the central unit to a minimum, smaller quantities of air are circulated than have traditionally been considered acceptable in large scale installations such as office blocks. Small air flow rates necessitate high temperatures in order to carry the required amount of heat. Delivery temperatures of over 170°F are not uncommon; almost all gas, oil and electric domestic units have delivery temperatures of 140° or more. This may be compared with supply air temperatures of between 90° and 120° which have for many years been used in offices, cinemas and other public buildings.

Room Heaters in General

Although we are primarily concerned with central heating — that is heating from one central point in the house where the fuel, whatever it may be, is converted into heat — there are now so many types of room heater on the market, many of them advertised as central heating, that consideration must be given to them. Some of them offer a cheap and satisfactory alternative to central heating. The rest of this chapter will therefore deal with room heaters. The electric heaters are suitable only for normal tariff supplies unless the contrary is stated.

High Temperature Radiant Heaters

These include the conventional coal fire, gas and electric fires and radiant oil fires. The feature common to all is the high temperature of the heat emitting surface, at about 1,500°F. At this temperature over 90 per cent of the heat emission is by radiation. Such heaters are therefore eminently suitable for producing local comfort in an otherwise unheated space. The radiation is unaffected by draughts and, except for the coal fire, the heaters can be turned on or off as occasion demands. Where they are intended for continuous use, many designs include secondary heat exchange surfaces to provide a higher proportion of convected warmth. Coal and gas fires may also have back boilers for domestic hot water or central heating, or both. An oil fired radiant heater with a back boiler, similar in appearance to a gas heater, is also available.

All high temperature radiant heaters provide a concentration of radiant heat with one asset which is always exploited but seldom referred to — a room occupant's ability to regulate the amount of heat he receives without interfering with other people's comfort, simply by moving nearer or further from the fire.

Electric Tubular Heaters

These are tubes about 2in in diameter containing a heating element. They may be run singly or in banks along walls at low level. They are cheap but not very elegant in appearance and they are normally only used in workrooms, garages and the like. The operating temperature of the tube is about 180°F, as with hot water pipes, and the emission is rather more convective than radiant. They may be controlled by a room air thermostat.

Electric Convectors

These may be either natural draught or fan convectors. Both types have high temperature heating elements. The outlet from the natural convector has to be near the top. This fact, in conjunction with the high outlet air temperature, tends to produce large temperature gradients in the room, the warmth at head level being much greater than at the floor. Fan convectors offset this tendency by delivering the warm air at floor level. Because of the greater air flow, the outlet air temperature is also lower for a given heater rating, so the temperature gradient in the room is not so marked. The output from both types of heater is entirely convective.

It might be thought that the fan convector is more expensive to run because of its electric motor. That is not so. Not only is the motor rating very small, but the whole of the current used by the appliance is ultimately converted to heat, as with any electrical or mechanical device which consumes power within a given space.

Oil Filled Radiators

These are similar in appearance to ordinary hot water radiators. They operate at a similar surface temperature and so have similar thermal characteristics. They contain oil which is heated by an electric immersion heater. The output is about 70 per cent convective and 30 per cent radiant.

Electric Panels

The type suitable for domestic heating is the low temperature panel, operating at a surface temperature of 180° to 200°F. It contains electric resistance elements embedded in a fibrous insulating material with a hard surface, usually fluted for stiffness. It has similar thermal characteristics to a single-panel hot water radiator. As with all electric heaters, panels should not be installed where there is a possibility of their being covered by curtains, hanging clothing or the like. That is because the surface, if covered, will build up a high temperature to dissipate the heat which is being generated internally, with a consequent risk of scorching or fire.

Simple Block Storage Heaters

These were invented to make use of off-peak electricity, available at night at cheaper than normal rates. The method is to heat a mass of refractory brick blocks which, cooling during the following day, give off the heat stored overnight. A booster charge may be added in the middle of the day. The blocks are enclosed in a sheet-metal case.

The principle is simple and there is little to go wrong. However, the heaters are bulky and very heavy, and the output from them is not controllable. Moreover a considerable proportion of the output is at night during the main charging period. This may not be a disadvantage in a heavily constructed building, where the indoor temperature does not vary a great deal between day and night. But for fuel economy in lightly constructed buildings, intermittent heating to some degree is essential. If such a building is to have block storage heaters then the controlled output type (see below) will probably prove more satisfactory, though more expensive to buy in the first place.

The output from a simple block storage heater varies with the surface temperature as it cools. For the average condition, and allowing for the conversion of radiant emission to convection at the back of the heater, about 65 per cent of the output is by convection and 35 per cent by radiation.

Controlled Output Storage Heaters

These were developed in the 1960s to deal with the chief shortcoming of the simple block storage heater — the lack of control. Once such a heater is charged nothing can be done to vary the output, no matter how the weather may change or what happens to the room temperature.

The controlled output heater has a refractory thermal storage core similar to the earlier version, and is similarly charged at off-peak times. However, the core has an air passage through it. This is connected by way of an electric fan to inlet and discharge openings in the casing. The whole unit is heavily insulated to reduce heat emission from the casing to a minimum. The output is by forced convection, the fan being under the control of a room thermostat. To eliminate uncontrolled natural convection through the core, the air passage is arranged in the form of an inverted U, with air inlet and discharge both at the bottom of the unit. When the fan is not running, any tendency for the air in the unit to rise as it picks up heat from the core merely traps it at the top of the inverted U. There is a bypass arrangement, with a damper, which mixes cool inlet air with the hot air from the core when the fan is running. The bypass damper is under the control of a thermostat in the discharge opening. Its function is to keep the delivered air at a steady predetermined temperature however hot the core may be. Some models include spigots for air duct connections to be taken to an adjacent room if required.

It will be seen that the controlled output storage heater is considerably more sophisticated in its design than its forerunner, and it is of course more expensive. It remains both bulky and heavy. There is a certain amount of heat emission from the casing, including some radiation, but the main part of the output is convective.

Electric Underfloor Heating

This is one of the electrical equivalents of panel heating. Like the hot water counterpart, it can only be incorporated into a new house or flat, as it is built into the concrete floor slab. The electrical variety is an off-peak system which uses the floor slab as the heat storage medium. It can only be used where there is a solid concrete floor. For an upper floor with joists and floorboards, some other form of heating must be installed — block storage heaters for instance.

The installation of underfloor heating is carried out during the building of the house when the lower layer of the ground floor slab has been cast and is set. Electric resistance cables are laid to a predetermined spacing across the floor slab of each room. They are then covered with the floor screed — the fine concrete which forms the top of the structural floor — the screed being smoothed and left to set in the usual way. At this stage the heating cables should be tested for electrical continuity to ensure that they have not been damaged during the screed laying. Removing wet concrete is easy; removing set concrete is not.

Floor finishes that are likely to be damaged by heat must not, of course, be used with any sort of floor heating. The restriction applies with greater force to electric systems than to hot water ones. With the latter the temperature of the floor cannot rise above the temperature of the water pipes in it, and this is limited by thermostatic control in the boiler room. With electric heating the buried cables generate heat at a constant rate whatever restrictions may be accidentally placed in the heat flow path. So a solid object on the floor surface may, if it is of high thermal resistance, cause a marked rise of temperature in the floor immediately beneath.

In the normal way the floor is charged with heat overnight. There may also be a booster charge in the middle of the following day. As with the simple block storage heater, once the floor is charged there is nothing that can be done to control the rate at which it gives up its heat. This is a shortcoming of the system. Attempts to meet it have been made by combining a time switch with an outdoor thermostat to delay the beginning of the charging period in accordance with the following day's anticipated temperature. This form of control must of course presuppose some predictable pattern for English weather.

Even if the heat charge at the beginning of the day is perfectly matched to the day's heat requirement, the heating of the floor and the steady cooling between periods of charge produce a temperature variation in the room. The floor screed thickness should be calculated to keep this room temperature swing within bounds, say within 6°F. To prevent foot discomfort the floor surface temperature should be limited to a maximum of 80°F.

Enough has probably been said to show that the design of an off-peak floor heating system should only be undertaken by those with a thorough understanding of the physical principles involved. Unfortunately this need has not always been realised by installers in the past.

The merits of underfloor electric heating are those of floor panel heating discussed earlier — complete invisibility, clear floor space, low room temperature gradients and a high mean radiant temperature. The mean output is about 45 per cent convective and 55 per cent radiative.

Electric Ceiling Heating

The electrical equivalent of ceiling panel heating, this is not an off-peak storage system, but one using current at normal rates under the control of a room thermostat. The heating element is of foil or a conducting silicone, enclosed between thin plastic or fibreglass sheets. It is produced in rolls which are stapled to battens or to the ceiling joists, with a thick backing of thermal insulation. The ceiling finish, which may be plasterboard, wood or a number of other materials, is then fitted below the heating sheet and fastened hard up against it. Care has to be taken with the fastening to ensure that the heating element is not damaged.

The system is intended to be installed in new buildings, but could no doubt be put into an existing one — at the cost of taking down the ceilings. It is a fairly new development and some electricity boards will only approve its installation in buildings which have been thermally insulated to a high standard. This does not imply any criticism of the system. The boards' requirement may possibly be a foretaste of more stringent future regulations applying to all forms of direct electric heating.

With a ceiling surface temperature of 100°F the emission is 65 per cent radiant and 35 per cent convected heat. See Chapter 6 for the limitations on surface temperature which should be observed.

Electric Heating Generally

Most of the room heating systems we have considered have been electric. There are reasons for this. Electricity is a clean fuel that can be easily transported to any point and converted to heat by means of a simple resistance element. Air is not needed for combustion and there are no fumes to be dissipated. Manufacturers are therefore constantly devising new ways of using it. It is however an expensive fuel. We shall see in the next chapter why this is so, and also how to assess its cost against that of other fuels.

The electric wiring for all types of heating system is carried out by electrical contractors. Electricity boards will not give a power supply to any electrical installation unless it has been carried out to their approval. This usually means by an approved contractor. He will normally work to the standard recommendations of the Institution of Electrical Engineers. All in all there should be little doubt about the quality of workmanship on the electrical wiring side.

However, all the varieties of heating system which use electricity as a fuel are also installed by electrical contractors. This means that unless the contractor employs a designer with general heating experience, the purchaser is likely to get a packaged scheme which may or may not suit his own particular needs. Some area boards meet this difficulty by employing their own heating engineers to design schemes to customers' requirements, the installation work being carried out either by their own staff or approved installers.

Chapter 5

Running Costs

The running cost of a house heating system will depend on a number of things. Some of these are:

(1) How big is the house?
(2) What shape is it?
(3) Which part of the country is it in?
(4) How much is the heating used?
(5) How much ventilation takes place?
(6) How well is the house insulated?

The first four questions can be answered more or less precisely, the last two only in general terms. And there are other questions not listed. So it is clear no simple formula can be devised which will give the exact running cost for any particular case. However, the prediction of *comparative* running costs — one fuel against another — for any given house is not difficult. That is because there is a clearly defined relationship between the various units in which fuel is sold, and an indisputable heat content, or calorific value, of each fuel.

This chapter has been devised to enable an estimate to be made of running costs, using the fuel prices prevailing in your own district. Where possible the characteristics of your own house will be used in answering the questions posed above. Where that would be impracticable, as for instance with the question on insulation, average domestic building construction will be assumed. Similarly, average winter temperatures will be taken. So if you live in Cornwall your fuel bills will be less than predicted, and if in Aberdeenshire more. If your house is well insulated you will achieve reductions on the predicted cost, and if it is a greenhouse you are likely to find the predictions optimistic. But, however your own particular case varies from the general, the cost *comparison* for alternative fuels will remain valid. The results can therefore be used as a guide in selecting the cheapest fuel for your house. Fuel cost is not the only criterion of course. Quite apart from personal preference, the capital cost — and capital charges — should be considered also. These are dealt with in Chapter 11.

The Useful Therm

Comparing the cost of one fuel with that of another seems to be less well understood than any other aspect of heating, so we start by setting out the relationship between all the common fuels. We assume first of all that each fuel can be consumed at 100 per cent efficiency, so as to get from it all the heat it possesses.

1 therm of coal gas or natural gas produces 100,000Btu
1 gallon of fuel oil produces 163,000Btu
1 hundredweight of coke produces 1,230,000Btu
1 hundredweight of coal produces 1,290,000Btu
1 hundredweight of anthracite produces 1,450,000Btu
1 unit of electricity produces 3,412Btu

Gas is sold by the therm, which is a quantity of heat, so the first entry above is a definition of the therm rather than information about the properties of gas. The figures for coke, bituminous coal and anthracite are average ones for normal condition as delivered. They vary with the type and moisture content. That for oil is for 35sec gas oil.

If we now take into account the efficiency of the fuel burning apparatus, which varies with the type of fuel, we can derive from the natural calorific values listed above the amount of each fuel which must be consumed to produce one *useful therm* of heat. Gas is sold in therms of heat content, but when the boiler or air heater efficiency is taken into account, in order to get one therm of *useful* heat, more than one therm's worth of gas must be bought. The same reasoning applies to every fuel. The useful therm — ie 100,000Btu of heat actually warming the house — gives us a common basis for comparison. If we know the price of gas per therm, coal per hundredweight, oil per gallon or electricity per unit, we have only to multiply that price by the appropriate quantity of fuel, derived as explained above, to know what we shall be paying per useful therm of heat. The whole operation can be reduced to reading a graph (see Fig 6, p 54).

We shall return to the price of the various fuels when we have established how much heat your particular house will need in the course of a year. The required amount of heat will be expressed in therms, so the price per useful therm will tell us the cost directly.

How Much Heat?

To make an estimate of the annual heat requirement we need to know the size of the house and something about its shape. We also need to know the number of hours per week the heating system is to be in use. We assume that ventilation is not excessive and that doors and windows fit well. If not, they should be dealt with before heating is installed. A certain amount of air will infiltrate in any case. And we want it to do so, since we need fresh air to breathe.

The fresh air has to be heated to room temperature. In addition to the heat required for this, heat is also needed to make good the continuous loss by conduction

Fig 5   Chart for approximate multiplication   Ignoring decimal points and any preceding or terminating noughts, join with a ruler the point on scale A representing the first number with the point on scale B representing the second. The product of the numbers is given where the ruler cuts the middle scale

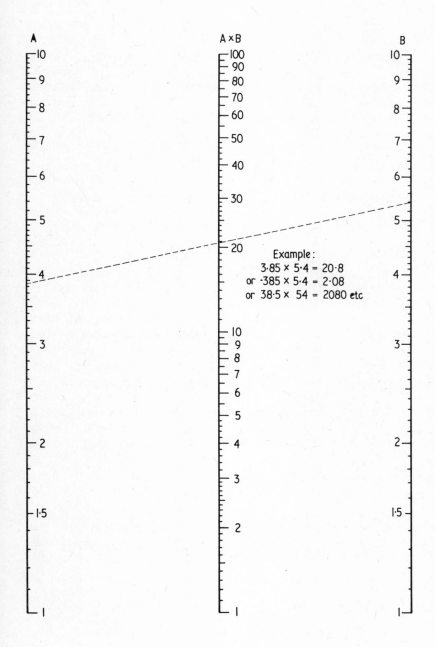

A

A × B

B

Example :
3·85 × 5·4 = 20·8
or ·385 × 5·4 = 2·08
or 38·5 × 54 = 2080 etc

49

through the fabric of the building from the warm interior to the cold outside. The amount of these heat requirements will vary not only with the type of house, but also with the outdoor temperature, being greatest in the depth of winter and least in autumn and spring. The variations can be averaged out, however, since we are here concerned with the total heat requirement through the winter. We proceed as follows — and here the reader will find a calculating aid such as a slide rule or the alignment chart of Fig 5 a help.

First work out the volume in cubic feet of the total heated space in the house. The floor area multiplied by the room height will give you the volume. We need this figure to determine the ventilation heat requirement.

Next work out the surface area in square feet of the *outside* walls of the house, from ground to eaves, including windows. For example if the perimeter of the house is 100ft and the wall is 16ft high the surface area is 1,600sq ft.

Now also work out the area of windows, the floor area of the ground floor and the ceiling area of the top floor, all in square feet. Count front door and back door as windows. If any ground floor rooms have no upper floor over them, include their ceiling areas under the third item as well as their floors under the second item.

Now, choosing either Table 2 or Table 3 according to your intended programme of use, multiply the volume of the house and each of the areas you have just worked out by the appropriate factor from the table. Add the answers, and you will have the total winter heat requirement — for heating only — in therms.

Table 2

Winter heating factors for a system in use all day, every day, but off at night

(1)	Heated volume factor	0.016
(2)	Outside wall factor	0.280
(3)	Window factor	0.520
(4)	Ground floor factor	0.160

(5a)	Upper floor ceiling factor for FLAT ROOFED HOUSE	0.320
(5b)	Upper floor ceiling factor for HOUSE WITH ATTIC SPACE	0.260
(5c)	Upper floor ceiling factor for HOUSE WITH INSULATED ATTIC SPACE	0.120

Table 3

Winter heating factors for a system in use mornings and evenings only during the week, all day at weekends, but off every night

(1)	Heated volume factor	0.010
(2)	Outside wall factor	0.170
(3)	Window factor	0.320
(4)	Ground floor factor	0.100
(5a)	Upper floor ceiling factor for FLAT ROOFED HOUSE	0.200
(5b)	Upper floor ceiling factor for HOUSE WITH ATTIC SPACE	0.160
(5c)	Upper floor ceiling factor for HOUSE WITH INSULATED ATTIC SPACE	0.073

You will notice that in Tables 2 and 3, three factors are given for the ceiling, according to the roof construction of the house. Choose the appropriate one for your case.

Example
What is the winter heat requirement of a house with a volume of 12,000cu ft, outside wall area of 2,000sq ft, window area of 200sq ft (including front and back doors), ground floor area of 800sq ft, upper floor ceiling area 800sq ft? The house has an insulated attic space and is heated mornings and evenings and all day at weekends.

Table 3 is the one we need, with (5c) as the ceiling factor. Using the factors, we have:
(1)   0.010 × 12,000 = 120

(2) 0.170 × 2,000 = 340
(3) 0.320 ×   200 = 64
(4) 0.100 ×   800 = 80
(5c) 0.073 ×   800 = 58
                Total 662

So the winter heating requirement is 662 therms.

Before converting this figure to a cost we need to add the HWS requirement. That will depend on the amount of hot water used, and on whether there are towel rails heated from the domestic hot water system. The total is also affected by the efficiency of the hot water cylinder insulation. We assume the cylinder is well lagged.

Table 4 tells you what your hot water requirements are likely to be. If all the family take daily baths, increase the tabulated figures by one-third. For every towel rail heated from the domestic hot water system add 1½ therms per week to the figures (ie an additional 45 therms to the winter total, and 33 therms to the summer).

Table 4

Heat needed for domestic hot water

Number in family	Therms per week	30 weeks winter total (therms)	22 weeks summer total (therms)
1	5.0	150	110
2	5.5	165	121
3	6.0	180	132
4	6.5	195	143
5	7.0	210	154
6	7.5	225	165

For every towel rail heated from the domestic hot water system, add 1½ therms per week to the tabulated figures.

We are now in a position to predict the total heating and hot water costs for winter and summer. The winter house heating requirement, computed from Table 2 or Table 3 as shown earlier, is added to the winter hot water requirement taken from Table 4.

Let us take our previous illustration with, for example, a family of four. From Table 4 the hot water needs of a family of four are 195 therms in winter and 143 in summer. We add 195 to our heating total of 662 therms, giving a total winter heat requirement of 857 therms. The summer requirement is for hot water only, and is 143 therms.

The Cost of the Heat

What will all this cost? The cost depends on the price of fuel and on how efficiently the heating boiler (or other apparatus) can release the heat that is locked up in the fuel. The graph in Fig 6 takes account of these factors, as explained at the beginning of this chapter, to give you the price per useful therm of heat.

To use the graph run a horizontal line from the fuel price on the left to meet the appropriate fuel line, then drop vertically to the scale of costs along the bottom. The broken line shows for example that coal at £1.40 per cwt costs 18p per useful therm. That is, it costs 18p for every therm of heat that is actually released into the heating system.

The heating and hot water requirements in therms, as worked out in the previous section, have to be multiplied by the price per useful therm, from Fig 6, to get the winter and summer running costs for your house.

Suppose for example that the owner of the house considered earlier uses coal, which he buys at £1.40 per cwt. Then his fuel bill works out as follows:

Winter: 857 therms @ 18p per therm = £154
Summer: 143 therms @ 18p per therm = £26

Multi-part Tariffs

Gas and electricity charges are often on multipart

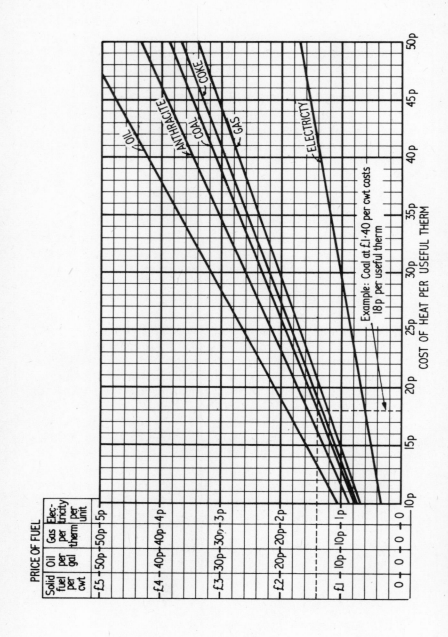

PRICE OF FUEL

Solid fuel per cwt	Oil per gal	Gas per therm	Electricity per unit
£5	50p	50p	5p
£4	40p	40p	4p
£3	30p	30p	3p
£2	20p	20p	2p
£1	10p	10p	1p
0	0	0	0

OIL

ANTHRACITE

COKE

COAL

GAS

ELECTRICTY

Example: Coal at £1·40 per cwt costs
18p per useful therm

COST OF HEAT PER USEFUL THERM

10p   15p   20p   25p   30p   35p   40p   45p   50p

54

tariffs, the cost per unit varying with the amount consumed in each quarter. In such cases it is useful to be able to predict the quarterly fuel consumption as well as the seasonal one. The winter fuel consumption for heating divides approximately as follows:

1 Oct — 25 Dec   35% of winter heating total
26 Dec — 25 March 55% ,,   ,,   ,,   ,,
26 March — 23 Apr 10% ,,   ,,   ,,   ,,

The fuel consumption for hot water remains constant throughout the year. The weekly figure in therms can be taken from Table 4 and multiplied by thirteen to get the quarterly amount.

All fuel consumption figures in therms must be multiplied by the price *per useful therm* from Fig 6 to get the running costs.

Electrical Heating Costs

Both on-peak and off-peak electricity convert to heat at 100 per cent efficiency. The electricity cost line in the graph allows for that. But off-peak room heater systems dissipate an appreciable part of their heat overnight. So the whole of the heat input is not available when it is needed on the following day. This means that an off-peak room heater system that heats the house adequately will cost more to run than is shown by the graph in Fig 6 and Tables 2 and 3.

The matter of electrical heating costs in general calls for a word of explanation. Why does electricity cost so much compared with other fuels for a given amount of heat? The reason is that power stations use the same

---

Fig 6 Cost of heat for various fuels The chart takes account of the price of the fuel, its heat content and the efficiency of the boiler, or other heat generator, to give the cost of the heat actually warming the house. The real costs of alternative fuels may thus be compared

fuels — oil and coal — that are burned in domestic heating installations. They use cheaper grades, but basically the same fuels. But whereas a domestic boiler can convert oil, coal or gas into heat at about 65 per cent efficiency, a power station converts its fuel into electricity at an efficiency of less than 30 per cent — in most cases about 25 per cent. This low figure is not because power stations are badly designed or run. It is a consequence of the laws of physics governing the conversion of thermal to mechanical energy. In a power station more than 70 per cent of the heat in the fuel is thrown away — some, as in the domestic boiler, up the chimney, but even more in the condenser cooling water of the steam turbines. When capital charges, distribution costs, salaries and other overheads are added, it is easy to see why electricity costs what it does. It is a highly refined form of energy. Degrading it directly to heat is a luxury that has to be paid for.

Incidentally, the heat that is lost to the condenser cooling water does not have to be thrown away. It can be used, in winter at least, to provide district heating near the power station. This is in fact done at Battersea in London. The overall thermal efficiency of the station can be raised to about 70 per cent by this means. It has been suggested that the waste heat could also be used agriculturally for soil warming. The only penalty for making the waste heat available at a higher, and therefore more useful, temperature, would be a slight loss in generator efficiency resulting from the necessarily higher power station condensing pressure. This drop in efficiency would be negligible compared with the useful heat saved.

The capital invested in generating plant is of course a big item in the generating board's accounts. Capital charges, including depreciation due to obsolescence, have to be met whether the plant is working fully or not. It therefore pays the board to keep the generators working round the clock if possible. Industry and private consumers use power mostly in the daytime, and the generators are sized to cope with this peak demand.

That means there is spare generating capacity at night. In order to keep as much of the plant as possible working round the clock, off-peak tariffs were introduced. They encourage the use of electricity at night by offering a cheaper unit rate so long as the current is taken between certain specified hours, usually 11pm and 7am. The original off-peak hours were later augmented by a midday boost. Electrical heating systems that are designed to operate on off-peak supplies must, of course, include some form of thermal storage. Most boards now offer a dual tariff — the 'white meter tariff' — which allows current to be taken at any time, but with lower rates for that taken overnight.

Chapter 6
The Installation

A heating installation, like any other artefact, can be well or badly made. When it is designed, as for domestic systems it almost invariably is, by the people who are going to install it, then a potential check is removed and there is scope for corner cutting or skimping which will probably not be in the best interest of the purchaser. It is the purpose of this chapter to set out the main requirements of a good installation. Safety, thermal efficiency and good appearance all have their claims. Automatic controls, where the choice between alternatives is a matter of preference rather than of good or bad practice, are dealt with in the next chapter.

Boiler and Hot Water Cylinder

The circulation of water from the boiler to the hot water cylinder can be either pumped or by gravity, as was mentioned in Chapter 2. Gravity circulation is that which can take place without the use of a pump, by natural convection of the water flowing to and from the cylinder. The water returned from the cylinder is cooler than that flowing to it and, provided the cylinder and its connections are above the level of the boiler, the difference in density of the water in the flow and return connections will produce a steady circulation.

To ensure that this is sufficient to heat the contents of the cylinder in the required time a simple calculation is, or should be, done. This determines the size of pipe necessary for the desired rate of flow. Unfortunately such a check is now seldom made. In most instances this does not matter; the customary 1in bore flow and return connections will be adequate. There are occasions, however, when the boiler and hot water cylinder are installed at or near a common level. Unless the connections are then run in such a way as to produce an adequate gravity circulating pressure, the cylinder will not heat up properly. Generally speaking this means that flow and return pipes must be larger than 1in bore, and must be run above boiler and cylinder level — perhaps in the roof space. Where boiler and cylinder are at a common level no gravity circulation whatever can take place if the connections are run below that level.

Cylinder connections for a gravity circulation must always be made direct to the boiler, never to heating flow and return pipes. The pressure drop along the pipeline of a pumped heating circuit is sufficient to interfere seriously with the very small gravity circulating pressure, and could easily stop the circulation of water to the cylinder or reverse it.

Where the circulation to the cylinder is pumped no problems of level arise. The heating pump is used for the purpose, and the connections to the cylinder are taken from the heating flow and return pipes in parallel with the heating circuit.

When the boiler is fired by solid fuel the primary circulation to the cylinder should always be by gravity. The reason for this is that coal or other solid fuel in a boiler has considerable mass and, in its incandescent state, a high heat content. If the heating circulating pump stops for any reason — including being switched off by a room thermostat — the boiler will continue for some time to supply heat to the water even though its own control thermostat cuts down the air supply to the combustion chamber. The hot water cylinder then acts as a thermal buffer or reservoir to absorb the additional heat. Clearly the cylinder could not do so if it relied on the heating pump, which by hypothesis is switched off, to convey the heat to it. The same situation does not arise with gas and oil fired boilers. There the burning fuel has negligible mass and the boiler output is immediately responsive to the control thermostat.

All domestic heating boilers suitable for installation in kitchens have smart stove enamelled casings. The casing may or may not contain thermal insulation, although it was originally provided as a protection for the insulation. With the smaller boilers it has now become mainly a form of attractive packaging, easily cleaned and similar to other kitchen fitments. Larger units, for installation in an outside boiler room, should always be insulated and preferably cased as well. There the emission from the boiler surface is simply wasted heat, and a metal casing alone is no substitute for proper insulation.

Solid fuel boilers must be provided with stoking and cleaning tools. In an outside or separate boiler room a wall rack should be provided for the tools.

The smoke pipe from an oil fired boiler should be fitted with a draught stabiliser (see p 32), and that from a conventionally flued gas boiler with a draught diverter (see p 32). When a gas boiler has a conventional flue the final outlet should be fitted with a GLC terminal, again as a protection against wind and downdraughts. The initials have nothing to do with London's local government, but survive from the days when the Gas Light & Coke Company was a household name. The boiler smoke pipe, which may be of vitreous enamelled cast iron or, in the case of gas, of asbestos cement, should be sealed at the connection to the chimney shaft by a packing of asbestos rope.

A fresh air inlet to the boiler room, of the size indicated in Chapter 3 (p 33), must be provided. If the kitchen window is used for this purpose it must be fitted with glass louvres so that the fresh air supply cannot be shut off.

The boiler should have a drain cock, so that the system can be emptied. The drain cock is best fitted with a hose union to enable a garden hose to be used to run the water to waste. A boiler room in a cellar or basement — or anywhere below the level of the house drainage system — must be provided with a sump, into which water is drained when emptying down. The sump should be fitted with a hand operated pump (similar to the semi-rotary bilge pump in a boat) with the discharge pipe run to the nearest surface drain.

A safety valve of ¾in bore should be fitted either to the boiler or to a flow pipe close to the boiler. No other valve should be interposed between the boiler and the safety valve, which should be set to open at a pressure dependent on the height of the feed tank. The following settings are appropriate for the feed tank heights indicated:

Up to 20ft height   15psi
20 to 30ft height   20psi
30 to 40ft height   25psi

When the boiler is subjected to the head of the pump (ie for the arrangement shown in diagram A of Fig 8, p 66), the safety-valve setting should be increased by the amount of the pump pressure. Settings higher than those listed above are sometimes recommended. There is no 'right' figure, but if the valve is to afford reasonable protection low settings are preferable to high ones.

An open vent pipe of 1in bore must be run from the boiler to above the feed tank, and a similar open vent run from the secondary (outflow) side of the hot water cylinder to above the cold water storage tank. No valve should be interposed between the boiler and its vent pipe or the cylinder and the HWS vent pipe.

Boiler controls are dealt with in Chapter 7, together with the automatic controls for the rest of the system.

In a house where central heating is being installed for the first time the existing hot water tank or cylinder will probably not be suitable for use in the new system. An indirect cylinder is essential, for the reasons given earlier, whereas the old one will be a direct cylinder — a simple container without a hot water heating element.

However, there are available prefabricated water/water heaters which can be fitted in a direct cylinder to convert it to an indirect one. They are of small bore and will only operate on a pumped circulation, with the advantages and disadvantages which that entails. Needless to say, an existing galvanised hot water tank or cylinder should not be used in a new copper system.

Unless the boiler is intended to run throughout the year, an electric immersion heater should be fitted to the hot water cylinder for summer use. This will have its own built-in control thermostat, completely independent of the heating system. An immersion heater must reach to near the bottom of the vessel it is intended to heat, *and so must the controlling thermostat element*. Otherwise only a fraction of the contents of the vessel will be heated. If the hot water cylinder is tall, a short immersion heater fitted horizontally near the bottom will be much more effective than a longer one fitted vertically from the top.

Hot water cylinders must be adequately insulated. An unlagged 30gal cylinder can dissipate ninety therms of heat a year, even in a warm airing cupboard.

Oil Fired Installations

The oil storage tank will normally be out of doors. If it must be indoors then the local fire regulations should be consulted to see what requirements have to be met. The tank must certainly be in a separate room from the boiler, and the door of the tank room must be partially bricked up or otherwise blocked off to form a catchpit greater in capacity than the tank.

The tank should always be raised off the ground, supported on brick or concrete piers, and arranged with a fall of about 2in from end to end. This is to allow sludge (water, mud and other sediment) to accumulate at the low end, where a sludge cock for drainage should be fitted. Water is heavier than oil, by the way. Roofing felt between the tank and the supporting piers will prevent damp rising and rainwater accumulating unseen to cause rusting. The tank, which will be made from sheet steel, should be painted externally, preferably with bitumastic or red lead paint. It should have a removable inspection cover, and must be fitted with a contents gauge. There are many varieties of these, but a simple transparent tubular sight gauge connected to the side of the tank, in which the oil level can be seen, is quite adequate. A gauge of this sort should incorporate some safety device, such as a spring-loaded valve, to prevent loss of oil from the tank if the gauge tube is accidently broken.

There will be an oil fill pipe and a vent pipe fitted to the top of the tank. The vent pipe should be turned over to keep out the rain. The fill pipe should have a removable screwed cap. Wherever the tank may be sited, if it is a rectangular one, the vent pipe must not be run up to a height much more than a foot above the top of the tank. When the tank is being filled oil is pumped in at a fairly high rate. If the tank should be overfilled the oil will run out of the vent pipe. If the oil has to rise several feet above the tank before it can run out, the tank will be subjected to a fluid pressure it was not designed to withstand and it will deform or burst. Cylindrical tanks — not normally used in domestic installations — are inherently stronger than rectangular ones, and the same restriction does not apply.

The feed pipe, run from the higher end of the tank to the oil burner, may be of black steel pipe or of copper. Galvanised pipe must not be used. If copper is used the joints and fittings should be of the compression type, not capillary. Steep pipe buried underground should be wound with protective waterproof tape throughout the buried length.

The oil feed pipe should be valved at the tank. A fire valve is fitted in the pipe at the point where it enters the building; this is to cut off the oil flow to the burner in the event of fire. The valve can be shut by a pivoted falling weight which is supported by a taut wire which passes over the oil burner. At this point in the wire there is a fusible link of low-melting-point alloy. Similar links can be included in any closed passage through which the feed pipe may run. In the event of fire at any of these points the nearest link melts and the deadweight drops, closing the fire valve.

A filter must also be included in the feed pipe. There are several varieties of these, those for domestic fuel oil having paper elements. If an additional valve is fitted before the filter, the element can be changed without mess.

The oil feed line should be coupled to the burner with a flexible armoured hose. This must be long enough to allow the burner to be moved for maintenance.

Feed and Expansion Tank

The tank can be of galvanised steel or of plastic. In a copper system, plastic is preferable. There must be an overflow pipe run to outside, and of course the mains water connection to the ball valve. For ease of maintenance there should be a stop cock before the ball valve. The system feed pipe is taken from the bottom of the tank. No valve of any sort should be fitted in the feed pipe.

The tank should have an extended-arm ball valve (see Fig 7) so that when cold the quantity of water in the tank is only just sufficient to float the ball.

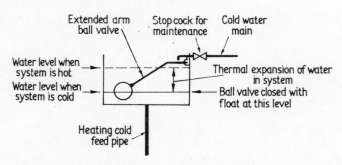

Fig 7   Feed and expansion tank

When the system is hot the tank fills, by way of the system feed pipe, and the ball is completely submerged. If the proper type of arm is not used water will be discharged from the overflow pipe whenever the system heats up. This will also happen if the tank is too small, an unlikely fault in a domestic installation since the 10gal minimum standard size will cope with installations of 90,000Btu per hour output.

The open vent pipe from the boiler — and any other open vents from elsewhere in the heating system — should be run to the feed tank and turned over the top. The HWS open vent pipe is turned over the top of the main cold water tank.

Circulating Pump

The calculation of the total resistance of the heating system to water flow and the selection of a pump to meet it is part of the design process which is outside the scope of this book. However, certain operational faults can be caused by the position of the pump in the system, and we shall consider these. The design errors which lead to these faults have occurred in the past and will no doubt occur again.

If pressure gauges were fitted to the pipework on either side of the pump — these are not necessary in domestic installations — they would show the effect of the pressure or 'head', produced by the pump when it is running. As we saw on p 16, this 'head' is the height, measured in feet, to which the pump would deliver water through perfectly smooth pipes if it were free to do so. In a closed circuit such as a heating system the pump is not free to lift the water in this way from one level to another. The whole of the pump head is used to overcome pipe (and similar) friction, the pressure dropping from the pump outlet all the way round the system to the pump inlet. Here the water enters the pump and is again raised in pressure by the impeller. A series of pressure gauges round the system would show the steady drop in pressure from pump outlet to pump

65

inlet. When the pump is running, any free water surface in a tank or a pipe will act as a pressure gauge, the water standing at a higher level if subjected to pressure or lower level if under suction. There are two such free water surfaces in a heating system. One is in the feed tank and the other in the open vent pipe from the boiler.

Consider diagram A of Fig 8. When the pump is not running, the water in the vent pipe obviously stands at the same level as the water in the feed tank. What happens when the pump starts? A pressure difference is produced across the pump of, say, 6ft head. A pressure gauge on the delivery side of the pump would therefore show 6ft of water pressure higher than a gauge on the suction side. But is this pressure difference produced by a delivery pressure increase of 6ft or by a suction pressure drop of 6ft, or by some other combination of the two? The first alternative is the correct one in the case we are considering. The pressure difference must show itself in the levels of the water standing in the feed tank and the open vent pipe. The water in the feed tank has only to drop by a fraction of an inch to provide enough water to raise the free surface in the vent pipe by the required six feet. So that is what happens. And,

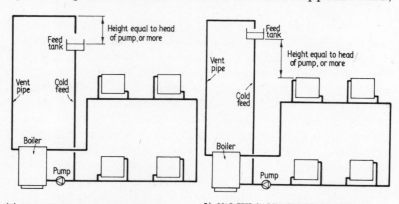

(A) COLD FEED ON SUCTION SIDE OF THE PUMP   B) COLD FEED ON DELIVERY SIDE OF THE PUMP

Fig 8   The effect of pump position   The system is subjected to pressure or to suction, according to the position in which the pump is fitted

if water is not to be continuously pumped out through the vent pipe, the pipe must be installed with its top at least 6ft (or whatever the pump head may be) above the level of the feed tank.

Now consider the arrangement shown in diagram B of Fig 8. Here the feed and vent pipes are both on the delivery side of the pump. Whatever happens to one pipe when the pump starts must also happen to the other. A moment's consideration will show that the level of water in the feed tank cannot be raised by the pressure of the pump. This could only be done by drawing a quantity of water from somewhere to fill the tank. And there is no such source available. So the water level in the feed tank stays where it is, and the pressure difference across the pump is produced by a drop in pressure on the inlet side. In this case, therefore, when the pump starts the whole system is put under suction, the intensity depending on the distance from the pump. At the pump outlet the pressure remains unchanged when the pump starts. But pipe friction produces a steady drop in pressure all the way round the system to the pump inlet, where the cumulative drop is equal to the full head of the pump. Here the water enters the pump and has its pressure restored to the outlet condition.

What is the effect of this on the system? If, under static conditions with no pump running, the water pressure at any point is greater than the head the pump can produce, then nothing untoward will happen when the pump starts. If, however, the static head at any point is less than the pump head, then starting the pump will produce sub-atmospheric conditions at that point and air will be sucked into the system through any opening it may find. Such openings include the key-operated air vents which are fitted to radiators. The use of the air vent under these conditions, instead of releasing air from the radiator, will cause more to be sucked in.

The cure, or rather the prevention, is to ensure that the static water pressure throughout the circulating

67

system is greater than the head of the pump. This means that the height of the feed tank must exceed the height of the topmost pipe or radiator by an amount at least equal to the head of the pump.

The requirements for the two cases are marked on Fig 8. Other pump positions will not call for special restrictions on the height of tank or vent pipe.

Pipework

Copper pipework is now almost universally used for domestic heating systems, for the reasons given in Chapter 2. The pipes should be installed neatly, with adequate supports. Copper is a weaker metal than steel and copper pipes have thinner walls, so they demand greater care against the possibility of damage. This applies chiefly in a boiler room or the roof space; in the heated rooms, where the pipes run along the walls, clip supports every few feet are all that is needed. Where pipes of any material pass through walls and floors, pipe sleeves should be built in to make a smooth neat hole. Cover plates, clipped to the pipe and covering the end of the sleeve, are sometimes fitted.

The movement of pipes as a result of thermal expansion is not usually great enough to pose serious problems in domestic installations. However, thermal expansion and contraction will take place whenever the system is heated or cools, and some attention should be given to it. A 100ft length of copper pipe expands by 1.58in when heated through 140°F — the sort of temperature variation to which it will be subjected in a heating installation. This expansion is not negligible. A straight run of pipe along the walls of two adjacent rooms may well be 30ft long. The resulting 0.48in of movement must be allowed for. If the pipe is fixed at the midpoint of its run, the movement will be divided, each end moving by ¼in approximately. If the pipe is fixed at one end, perhaps by the wall at the change of direction, the other end will move by the full 0.48in. If at that end a pipe support is so close to the corner that it prevents free movement, the support may be pushed out of the wall, or the pipe may bow along the straight run, or it may buckle. In one way or another the expansion will occur and it is best that it should be foreseen and allowed for.

General requirements are that pipe support clips should not grip the pipe too tightly, and that they should not be too close to changes of direction. If a long run is necessary, an expansion loop can often be arranged at some point in its length (see Fig 9).

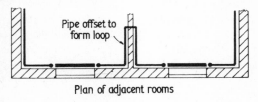

Plan of adjacent rooms

Fig 9   Expansion loop

Pipes must be run in such a way that air locks cannot form. This means that the highest point in any length of pipe should have some provision for the release of air, whether this be another branch pipe from the top, a radiator, or a specially installed air cock. Similarly a drain cock for emptying down must be provided at all low points.

All pipes that are not providing useful heat should be insulated. These include pipes in a boiler room, in floor ducts and in the roof space.

Valves

Each radiator or other heater should be fitted with two valves. One is to regulate the quantity of water flowing through the heater, an operation carried out during the commissioning of the installation. To ensure that the setting is not interfered with in day-to-day use this valve has no handwheel and can only be operated by a key. The other valve has a handwheel and can be opened or shut as the room occupants wish. The flow of water through the heater is of course completely stopped by the closing of one valve.

Isolating valves should be provided on the flow and return connection from the boiler to the hot water cylinder.

Air cocks, operated by a key, or automatic air vents, self-operating, must be fitted at high points as mentioned in the previous section. Where radiators or convectors are the highest part of the circulatory system no extra provision is needed. They have their own air cocks. The purchaser must be provided with keys to fit these and any other key-operated devices. It is worth pointing out here that the commonest cause of inadequate heat output from a radiator is air-locking. The symptoms are a cold top and a hot bottom.

Radiators

Steel panel radiators are supported either by two bottom brackets with a steadying bracket at the top, or by long concealed brackets at the back. Radiators over 6ft long should have three main supports instead of two.

Cast-iron radiators are supported by bottom brackets and a steadying stay near the top. Alternatively they can be supplied with feet. This saves the building in of brackets, but the legs are an obstruction on the floor, and they are too short to allow the heating main to be run in the best position.

Radiators should not project above window sills. When they do they are an obstruction as well as being unsightly.

No radiator should be longer than shown in Tables 5 and 6. Most installers seem unaware of any limitation on radiator length, so the reason for it should perhaps be given here. When the radiator valve is shut, the radiator drops to room temperature while the pipe beneath remains hot; thus the radiator contracts in length and the pipe does not. This bends the radiator connections, the amount of the bending being proportional to the length of the radiator. The bending stress in the connections reaches the safe working maximum for copper or for steel at the radiator lengths and heights shown in the tables. The figures are for radiators with top and bottom connections at opposite ends.

Table 5

Maximum radiator lengths for heating installations using copper pipe

Maximum radiator length (in)

Radiator nominal height	Radiator with $3/8''$ bore conections	Radiator with $1/2''$ bore connections	Radiator with $3/4''$ bore connections	Radiator with $1''$ bore connections
12"	44	34	23	16
18"	98	77	53	39
24"	173	136	94	70
30"	267	210	147	110

Table 6

Maximum radiator lengths for heating installations using steel pipe

Maximum radiator length (in)

Radiator nominal height	Radiator with $3/8''$ bore connections	Radiator with $1/2''$ bore connections	Radiator with $3/4''$ bore connections	Radiator with $1''$ bore connections
12"	41	32	25	19
18"	92	72	57	45
24"	161	128	101	80
30"	250	199	158	125

The tables must not be used to determine the size of radiator connections. The figures are a check on the maximum permissible length of radiator once the connections have been sized. If in a given application the required radiator would exceed the tabulated length, there are two courses open. Either a deeper radiator, with more columns or an extra panel, should be chosen; or two radiators can be used instead of one.

The restriction on length applies only when the heating main which serves the radiator runs beneath it. Other positions of the main produce a more flexible arrangement of the connections. In such cases both flow and return connections can be made at the bottom of the radiator if preferred.

Radiators are usually installed below windows. When they are not, the convected warm air tends to mark the wall above the radiator with dust. A shelf fitted above the radiator will prevent this.

Panel Heating Systems

The surface temperature of heated floors should not exceed 80°F. Some people find this too high for comfort over a period of time and would put the limit a few degrees lower.

Maximum wall temperatures depend partly on how many walls are heated; high levels of radiation coming from only one side produce a sense of thermal imbalance. An acceptable limit for one wall is 105°F. Where more than one wall is heated the additional surface will permit comparatively low rates of emission per unit area, so the limit of 105° can in practice be applied in most cases.

The effect of ceiling temperature on comfort has been investigated over many years. A number of factors are involved, the two most important being ceiling area and room height. Suitable maximum temperatures for normal room sizes are 92°F for ceilings 8ft high, 100° for those 9ft high, and 107° for those 10ft high.

The limitations on surface temperature given above do not, of course, take into account calculated heat losses. If the room heat losses (Chapter 8) cannot be met in full because the panel temperature would exceed the recommended maximum, then some additional source of heat must be provided in the room.

All ground floors transmit heat from the room air to outside. With a solid floor the heat flow follows a curved path down into the earth and up again to the outside ground surface. The outer edges of a floor lose more heat than the area in the middle of a room because a shorter heat flow path increases the rate of transmission. The heat loss from this cause becomes a serious consideration when the floor itself is used for heating, because then the floor temperature is much higher than usual. The outside edges of floors used in floor-warming schemes must therefore be insulated, and the insulation should preferably be taken down a foot or more to reduce the flow of heat through the ground. The damp-proof membrane below the floor slab must of course be carried down below such insulation.

Wall panel heating is best installed on internal walls for maximum fuel economy, though at some sacrifice of thermal balance. On an internal wall there is no back loss if the adjacent room is heated from the same partition wall. If it is not, the back loss contributes to its heating. When wall panels are installed on the outside walls of a room, insulation must be applied first.

Corrosion Inhibitors

There always have been mixtures of metals in heating systems. But in the days when radiators were invariably of cast iron and the only non-ferrous metal was in the gunmetal or brass of the valves, corrosion was less of a nuisance than it can be now, with steel radiators and copper pipes. A corrosion inhibitor is therefore worth having, particularly in microbore systems where any sediment can easily clog the water flow.

Warm Air Systems

Air delivery temperatures with these systems are always high. The only thing the purchaser can do, if he wants to keep room temperature gradients as small as possible, is to choose a unit with the maximum air flow rate for the required output of heat. This may mean a slightly noisier heater, but he would be well advised in any case to hear the unit of his choice in operation before committing himself.

Air noise in ventilation systems is caused partly by the fan and partly by the speed of air flow in the ducts.

The air flow component is increased and the fan component reduced by sharp elbows, angles and offsets in the duct run. For domestic systems, which are always compact, air speeds in ducts should not exceed 500ft/min. Chapter 9 includes a chart giving duct sizes for various rates of flow.

Supply air outlets should be 'registers'. These are grilles which incorporate some form of flow control damper. They can be in floors or walls, those in floors requiring attention to be kept clean. Wall registers in a good quality installation may have adjustable louvres to control the lateral and vertical distribution of the air blown into the room.

One of the unfortunate consequences of high delivery air temperatures is that outlet speeds from wall registers have to be fairly high to project the very buoyant air across the width of the room. However, the outlet speed should not exceed 300ft/min, taken over the face area of the register (Chapter 9). Higher air speeds are usual for return air grilles, but they should not exceed 400ft/min. The heating or electrical contractor's quotation will probably not state the air speeds on which the design is based. He should be able and willing to give the information if asked.

If a fresh air inlet connection is made to the system, the inlet should be well away from the heater flue outlet. This consideration should only arise when the heater has a balanced draught flue. Return air ducts should not be run from bathroom, WC or kitchen.

Air ducts must be made from galvanised steel, never from black sheet, and joints should be sealed with adhesive tape. Prefabricated ducts for domestic installations are made from steel 0.028in thick. This thickness is adequate for its purpose, but it will not stand much maltreatment without deforming. Careless concrete pouring and spading can crush underfloor ducts, reducing the cross-sectional area considerably. This sort of thing can only be prevented by adequate site supervision. Some measure of protection is given by a hard-setting thermal insulation which is available. The ducting is marketed with the insulation already applied.

All ducting should be insulated except where the heat emitted from the surface can be considered useful. Ducts in floor slabs should be waterproofed outside the insulation.

Warm air units are sometimes fitted in cupboards. When this is done precautions should be taken against the warping of the cupboard door from the heat. It may be lined with asbestos. Openings can be made at the top and bottom of the door to permit the circulation of air.

When a warm air system is to be installed in an existing house, measures must be taken to prevent the escape of room air up existing chimneys. This applies to some extent to all central heating systems, but the need is obviously greater with those employing warm air as the heating medium. A damper should be fitted in the flue from each fireplace, so that the chimney can be closed when the central system is operating. If open fires are not going to be used again, the chimney can be blocked permanently and the fireplace removed. Builder's work such as this is not normally included in the heating contract.

Chapter 7

Automatic Controls

Thermostats

Thermostats are the detecting element in a temperature control system. There are other detectors for other forms of control — pressure sensitive devices in pressure control systems for instance — but they need not concern us.

A thermostat is a simple device which performs quite a complicated task. It measures the temperature of the controlled medium (air or water or burner flame, or whatever it may be), it compares the measured temperature with a pre-set temperature — which is usually adjustable — and it sends a signal to the heating, cooling or other apparatus as a result of the comparison it has made. The temperature detector is usually a specially shaped element, made of two dissimilar metals, which deforms with temperature change. The deformation may make or break a simple electrical contact (on-off control), or may be used in conjunction with a balancing device elsewhere in the control system to regulate the output of a heater, in proportion to the amount of temperature error the thermostat element has detected (proportional or modulated control). Other more elaborate modes of control are available, but they are not used in domestic heating.

Burner Controls

Boilers and burners for all fuels are supplied complete

with their own automatic and safety controls. These vary from one type and make to another, but the essential in a wet system is the control of the fuel firing rate to maintain a selected water flow temperature from the boiler. This control is carried out by a thermostat which measures the flow temperature. In addition there may be a limit thermostat to cut the firing if a high water temperature is reached. This is a back-up safety device for the normal control thermostat and it is set at a higher temperature.

Gas and oil fired boilers and warm air units have their own safety controls to guard against flame failure and explosion. They include a detector to cut the fuel supply if the flame goes out, or fails to ignite when it should. A built-in time delay ensures that the combustion chamber and flue are cleared of explosive vapour before the ignition sequence can start again.

All the foregoing controls are supplied as part of the boiler or warm air unit. In addition there are the system controls which the purchaser chooses for himself and for which he will be charged separately by the heating contractor. We shall be chiefly concerned with these.

Boiler Flow Temperature

The boiler thermostat is an on-off controller normally set to give a flow temperature of 180°F in winter. The setting is sometimes adjusted to a lower level in mild weather. It is doubtful if changing the setting achieves much in the way of fuel saving except where no room-temperature control exists. Most installations will have a room thermostat or the equivalent to ensure that rooms are not overheated. In these circumstances the only saving made by reducing the boiler flow tempera-ture is in the small amount of heat emitted from insulated pipes in ducts and roof space.

On-off Room Temperature Control

The simplest way of controlling the system output is

by stopping and starting the heating pump. The living room or some other representative area is chosen as the controlling space, and a thermostat is installed there — on an internal wall. The kitchen, with all its stray heat gains, is obviously not a good place to choose for this purpose. The thermostat switches the heating pump on and off to maintain the room temperature at the selected level. The thermostat may be set to a lower temperature overnight.

The effect of stopping the pump is of course to stop water circulating through the boiler as well as through the rest of the system. The water in the boiler then rises in temperature, causing the boiler control thermostat to cut off the burner, or the air supply in the case of a solid fuel boiler. This condition lasts until the boiler water temperature drops sufficiently to start the burner. If the pump is still not running when this happens, the water temperature rise in the boiler will be rapid and the burner will cut out again. As soon as the room thermostat calls for heat and starts the pump, cool water is returned from the system to the boiler and the boiler thermostat starts the burner again. The system is simple and very widely used.

A drawback is that the control of the heating for the whole house is based on the temperature in one room. This may not always be truly representative. Sunshine, the wind in one particular quarter, the number of people in the room can all affect the room temperature. So the thermostat may switch off the pump when another room is not at the design temperature.

One way of meeting the difficulty is to put a thermostat in every room. This can open or close an electrically operated (solenoid) valve in the heating main to the room. With some piping layouts this is not possible, of course. Alternatively, in a radiator system, each radiator can be fitted with a thermostatically controlled valve. These are self-operating, need no electric connections, and are installed in place of the usual handwheel valve.

Modulated Temperature Control

Another way of meeting the difficulty is to regulate the flow temperature to the whole of the pumped system in accordance with the outdoor temperature. This is known as an outside compensated system. If the correlation between weather and flow temperature is correctly made, every room should get the heat it needs. If exceptional heat gains arise in any particular room the occupants can turn off the heaters by hand. Other rooms will not be affected by this action which, in any case, should be the exception rather than the rule.

It is not difficult to decide what the flow temperature should be for any outside temperature. The figures will not be the same for radiators and convectors because the two types of heater have different emission characteristics. But in either case a schedule of required flow temperatures can be drawn up corresponding to all outside temperatures. When such a schedule has been drawn up all that remains is to regulate the flow temperature in accordance with it. To attempt to regulate the boiler to achieve this would be difficult. The boiler is therefore left under its normal control, delivering water at 180°F, or whatever the design flow temperature may be, and the regulation is carried out by mixing some of the cool water returned from the heating system with the flow from the boiler, and pumping this mixture round the system. The arrangement is shown in Fig 10.

The mixing valve has two inlet connections and one outlet. It regulates the proportions of the mixture it delivers by closing off one inlet port as it opens the other, the movement being controlled by the valve motor. The motor, which may be electric or self-operated, is under the control of thermostat T_f in the flow pipe a little way downstream from the valve. Whatever temperature T_f may be set to, the valve will produce — so long as the temperature lies somewhere between the two inlet water temperatures. And that must always be the case. All that remains is to arrange

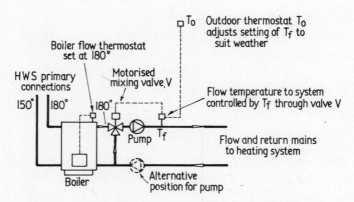

Fig 10 Outside compensated temperature control The heat
output of the system regulates itself automatically to
suit the weather

that T_f shall be set to the appropriate temperature for
the prevailing weather. This is done by varying the
setting by means of another thermostat T_0, fitted out of
doors. This setting operation is governed by the schedule
of flow temperatures appropriate to the system.

Tables 7 and 8 show suitable control schedules for those
radiator and convector installations which have a
winter design flow temperature of 180°F with an outside
temperature of 30° and a mean room temperature of
65°.

Table 7

Outside compensated control for radiator systems

Outside temperature °F	System flow temperature °F
30	180
40	152
50	124
60	96

Convectors include skirting heaters and sill-line heaters.
Fan convectors should not be supplied under the
modulated flow temperature system, or they will sometimes be a nuisance by blowing cold air. A single fan

Table 8

Outside compensated control for convector systems

Outside temperature °F	System flow temperature °F
30	180
40	154
50	128
60	102

convector in an otherwise modulated system may be supplied at boiler flow temperature, the flow connection to the convector being taken off upstream of the mixing valve. The fan convector will have its own thermostat, controlling the fan. If there are several they should have their own independent pump; otherwise the comparatively hot water returned from them will jeopardise the operation of the modulated temperature system.

Panel Systems

A panel heating system operates at a much lower flow temperature than other wet systems. For reasons given in the next section it is best to achieve the required flow temperature by a modulating control similar to that we have been considering. Typical temperatures might be as shown in Fig 11. Additional flow and return connections for a constant temperature circuit, if this should be required, are shown in broken line. The panel flow temperature can itself be controlled in accordance with the outside weather. The schedule for this depends on the panel system design, so cannot be included here.

Care must be exercised in mixing other heaters with a panel system on a single pump, for reasons similar to those limiting the use of fan convectors. If the unmodulated load is too large, the mixed return water temperature may be higher than the desired panel flow temperature and control of the panel system will be lost. Where there is more than one secondary heater, separate return pipes with two separate pumps may have to be used, one for the panel system and the other for the secondary heaters.

81

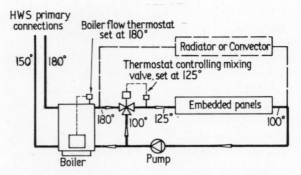

Fig 11 Panel heating temperature control   The automatically
controlled mixing valve provides low temperature
water for embedded panel heating, while the boiler
runs at its optimum working temperature

The Hot Water Cylinder

All the control methods considered leave the boiler
flow temperature unaltered at 180°F, or whatever it
may be. This has two advantages. In the first place the
boiler is designed to operate at that temperature and
does so more efficiently there than at any other.
Secondly, the domestic hot water cylinder receives
water from the boiler at 180° no matter what the
heating system may be doing. The rate of heating of the
cylinder is therefore not affected by house heating
requirements.

If the circulation to the cylinder is pumped, the
cylinder is at the mercy of the heating system unless
the heating controls are such that the pump runs
continuously. There are dual control arrangements
which allow either the cylinder or the heating thermostat
to control the pump, but when the two controllers are at
odds one must be allotted preference. All in all, whatever the system of heating controls, the most satisfactory
way to heat the hot water cylinder is by gravity
circulation. It will be remembered that, where the boiler
burns solid fuel, pumped primary connections to the
cylinder are not permissible at all.

Some provision should be made to control the cylinder temperature or it will sometimes be excessive. The maximum temperature for domestic hot water if furring of pipes is not to become a nuisance is 150°F. Water at this temperature must be considerably diluted with cold before it can be used in baths, sinks or basins. The hot water cylinder may therefore be controlled at any temperature between 130° and 150°.

Control thermostats for hot water cylinders are made to fit on the outside of the shell, being held in place by a circumferential strap. The thermostat should be fitted at a level a little above the boiler return connection. In practice it is often fitted so high on the shell that the effective hot water storage capacity of the cylinder is reduced to a fraction of its intended value. The thermostat can control a solenoid valve in either the flow or return connection. Where, as is common with a gravity circulation, the flow connection to the cylinder forms part of the boiler open vent pipe, the solenoid valve must be fitted in the return. When the water in the cylinder reaches the pre-set temperature at the level where the thermostat is fitted, the solenoid valve closes and circulation to the cylinder stops.

For gas and oil fired systems this arrangement is satisfactory. Clearly it will not do as it stands for a solid fuel system for, once the solenoid valve has closed and circulation stops, the value of the cylinder as a thermal reservoir is lost. One way of meeting the difficulty is shown in Fig 12. Instead of connecting the cylinder

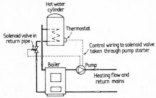

Fig 12 Thermostatic control for hot water cylinder with solid fuel boiler   The solenoid valve can close only when the pump is running, thus ensuring that the cylinder can act as a heat reservoir for the mass of fuel in the boiler whenever the pump is switched off

thermostat directly to the solenoid valve, the wiring is taken through the pump starter, so that the valve can only close when the pump is running. When the room thermostat stops the pump the solenoid valve opens, and the cylinder can act as the thermal reservoir for the residual heat in the boiler. This heat will of course raise the cylinder temperature. If the thermostat is set at about 135° the final temperature will still be within the required limit. Without the thermostat no such assurance is possible.

Dry Systems

Room heaters can only be thermostatically controlled room by room, though, as we have seen, some underfloor electric heating installations do use an outdoor thermostat to control the period of charge for the whole house.

Central warm air systems are controlled by a thermostat in one chosen room. This usually operates the burner, the fan starting and stopping according to the air temperature in the heat exchanger. Those units which incorporate a water heater will have separate controls for this. With electric thermal-storage central units the room thermostat stops and starts the fan. Controlling the heating for the whole house from one room in this way has the disadvantages already discussed in connection with wet systems. With warm air heating there is no readily available method of overcoming the disadvantages.

Time Switch Controls

Running costs will be reduced if room temperature levels are reduced or the heating switched off completely when not required. This means switching off the heating system or setting back room temperature levels overnight. On the following day the heating must be started early in order to bring the heating system and the structure of the building up to working temperature by daytime. No one enjoys rising in the small hours in midwinter to switch on the heating, so a time switch is employed for the purpose.

Time switches contain an electric clock and a number of switches operated by the clock. The switches can be set to any desired time and can be wired to the controls of any piece of apparatus. They can therefore be used to start pumps, fire boilers, switch on a complete control system, or to switch any of these off. Some, with a weekly cycle as the basis, can provide early switching on one day or one day's omission of operations. The variety of possible uses is so great that no purpose would be served in trying to list them.

A domestic heating system may be operated in the same way for seven days a week, or for five days with a different programme at the weekend. A simple day-based time switch will control the first of these. The second will need a controller on a seven-day basis, or a daily one with a manual selector switch to change the operation times on the Friday evening. There are many 'programmers' which incorporate such selector devices, though most of these are for dividing the boiler output between the heating and domestic hot water systems according to some prearranged timetable.

Probably the commonest use of the time switch in house heating is in controlling the heating pump. The boiler is allowed to run through the night, under the control of the boiler thermostat, to heat the domestic hot water. At a pre-selected time in the morning the time switch starts the pump; the HWS cylinder is well up to design temperature and the whole output of the boiler is available for the heating system.

Such an arrangement will only work where the cylinder is fed by a gravity circulation. If its heating is dependent on the pump, then either the boiler must deal with both the heating and the hot water simultaneously or one of the programmers mentioned above can be used, in conjunction with a three-way valve, to divert the flow to one or the other at pre-selected times.

A time switch can be used in conjunction with one or more outdoor thermostats to select the most economical pre-heating time according to the weather. The principle is shown in Fig 13, where two thermostats are used to provide three possible preheating periods. Thermostat T_1 is set at 35°F and thermostat T_2 at 45°. At 4 o'clock in the morning the first contact in the time switch closes. If the outdoor temperature is at 35° or below, the thermostats will both have closed and the electric supply will, with the closing of the time switch, be switched via T_1 to start the heating system. If the outside temperature is above 35°, thermostat T_1 will be open and no control action will be initiated. At 5 o'clock the second contact in the time switch closes also. If the temperature is at 45° or below, thermostat T_2 will be closed and the heating will be started on the closing of the time switch. If the temperature is above 45° both the thermostats will be open and the heating will not be started until the third contact closes at 6 o'clock.

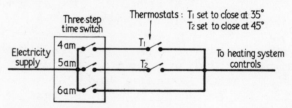

Fig 13 Variable pre-heating time control Three possible pre-heating periods are provided, the appropriate one being selected automatically by the two outdoor temperature thermostats

Interlocks

It is sometimes desirable that one piece of plant should not operate unless another item is already working. For instance where an installation is entirely dependent on pumped circulation, the boiler should not be fired unless the pump is working. To ensure this, the boiler/burner controls are interlocked with the pump. This merely means that the control wiring for the burner is looped through the pump starter in such a way that the burner can only fire when the pump is already switched on. Another example of an interlock was shown in Fig 12, p 84. There it was between the heating pump and a solenoid valve.

Frost Protection

In a wet system precautions must be taken against frost. Thermal insulation will delay the onset of freezing; it will not prevent it. If the temperature remains low enough for long enough, still water will eventually freeze. A frost protection thermostat may be installed indoors or out of doors. Its function is to start the heating system, overriding the time switch to do so, if the temperature falls near to freezing. Sometimes the thermostat is arranged to start the heating pump only, without firing the boiler. Moving water will not freeze so readily as still water, particularly when the circulation is through rooms warm from recent heating.

There is an advantage in putting the frost thermostat indoors, provided it is then located in the coldest possible spot. There it will only operate when it is really needed, that is to say when the roof space (where it is often installed) has dropped in temperature to a critical level. If it operates by starting the heating, as soon as the roof space is at a safe temperature it cuts the heating off. The minimum amount of fuel is used. An outdoor thermostat will initiate action as soon as the outdoor temperature is in the low thirties without regard to what the temperature is indoors, and it will continue the protective action for as long as the outdoor temperature remains low.

Using the circulating pump as a frost protection device is not sufficient unless the heating system is in day-to-day use. If the installation is likely to be left cold for several days in winter, more positive protection is needed, and the boiler must provide it. If a house is to be left unoccupied and unheated for some weeks in winter it is best that the heating system be drained down completely.

Chapter 8

Heat Losses

In Chapter 5 we looked at the comparative running costs for various fuels in a given house. That called for an estimate of the seasonal heat requirement of the house, based on the shape and assumed construction. Such an estimate is sufficient for the comparison of running costs through an average season, and therefore suitable for the purpose of selecting a fuel, but we need a more precise assessment of individual room heat requirements to specify room heater sizes and the total boiler (or other heater) duty.

These room heat requirements are calculated by the heating contractor when he prepares his tender. The calculation may therefore be left entirely in his hands. However if, as we advise, the house owner approaches several installers for competitive quotations, he may wish to check that the lowest priced scheme will actually produce the conditions required. Where heating and electrical contractors quote in competition it is perhaps even more important that the purchaser should be sure that the alternatives will produce the same result. Only by knowing what the heat requirements are can he make an informed decision. This chapter has been written to provide him with that knowledge.

The assessment of heat losses calls for a certain amount of arithmetic. This has been reduced to a minimum. What remains may be found less tiresome if Fig 5, p 49, is used for the multiplication. Pinpoint accuracy will not be achieved; nor is it necessary.

What are Heat Losses?

The heat loss of a room is the rate of heat input that is needed to maintain it at a steady temperature above that of its surroundings. It is literally the amount of heat being lost in each hour to the surroundings through the fabric of the room — the walls, floor and ceiling — and through air interchange with outside. It may be expressed in British thermal units per hour or in kilowatts, but the essential characteristic is that it expresses a steady rate of energy dissipation.

The energy dissipation has to be made good, and it is the function of the heating system to do that. Under steady conditions the heat input to a room exactly balances the heat loss from it. If a room heater is too small the room temperature will not reach the desired level, but will come to a balance at some lower point where the heat loss from the room — which depends on the indoor-outdoor temperature difference — is just equal to the emission from the heater in the room. Clearly the room heaters and the system as a whole must be sized to cope with the heat losses of all the rooms in the house under the most adverse conditions. In mild weather the output can be reduced to match the reduced heat losses, but the system must be capable of meeting the worst that can befall.

In fact it must be capable of more than this, for the following reason. If the heating is reduced overnight or at other times when it is not needed in full, then both the heating system and the structure of the house cool down. When full heating is needed again, the heating system, together with the bricks and mortar of the house, must be reheated to their normal operating temperatures. If the system were designed so that it just met the steady-state design heat loss of the house then it would take an indefinitely long time for design room temperatures to be attained, since part of the heat input would constantly be diverted towards bringing the system and the structure up to normal working temperature.

To allow for this the central plant — boiler or air

heater — is made larger than would be needed to meet the heat losses alone. However, the room heaters — radiators or the like — are not given a similar margin. The additional output required from them comes from the larger radiator-room temperature difference that exists during the heating-up phase. In the coldest weather this can be augmented by a higher than normal boiler flow temperature, made possible by the spare boiler capacity.

Design Temperatures

The heating system is required to maintain a room air temperature specified by the purchaser when the outdoor temperature is at some other specified level — usually 30°F. During those periods when the outdoor temperature drops below 30°, either the indoor temperature will fall below the specified level or — with a wet system — the additional boiler capacity included for heating-up purposes can be used to boost the water temperature to a higher level than usual to maintain design room conditions. Protracted periods of temperatures below 30° are not common anywhere in Britain. In Scotland and the more exposed parts of northern England a design outside temperature of 27° may be used.

Where the heating is chiefly by convection, including ordinary radiators, most people find the following room temperatures satisfactory:

Living and dining rooms	70°
Kitchen	65°
Bedrooms	60°
Hall, staircase, landing	60°
Bathroom, lavatory	65°

Panel heating systems will produce comparable comfort at lower room air temperatures than these. Precise figures cannot be given because they will vary with the mean radiant temperature of the room, and that depends on the room shape and the relative positions and temperatures of all the room surfaces. However, it is broadly true to say that room air temperatures between three degrees and five degrees lower than those listed should be satisfactory in a panel heated room.

The higher the room temperature the more costly the system will be to run. It is not always appreciated how much the choice of room temperature affects running costs. If we take an average winter outdoor temperature of 45°F, then, remembering that the heat loss from a room is proportional to the difference between indoor and outdoor temperature, we see that to maintain a room at 70° instead of 65° the fuel needed will be proportional to a 25° temperature difference (70°—45°) instead of a 20° (65°—45°) one. The increase in fuel consumption will therefore be about 25 per cent. In point of fact the relationship is not quite so simple as we have assumed — fortuitous heat gains from sunshine, electric lights and the room occupants complicate the issue — but the general principle holds.

Heat Loss Calculations

In the calculation of heat losses each room is treated individually. The volume of the room is worked out and an allowance of one air change per hour is made. This is the amount of air from outdoors which the heating system must raise to the specified room temperature. Where there are a number of people in a room, more than one air change per hour may be desirable; but the warmth given off by the people themselves (enough from each person to heat 500cu ft of air per hour from 30° to 70°) will provide sufficient heat for the additional ventilation, so the heating system need only cope with one air change per hour.

In addition to the ventilation heat loss there is the loss resulting from the conduction of heat through the building structure from the warm inside to the cold outside. The amount of this loss depends on the thermal transmittance of the wall, floor or ceiling, on its area and, once again, on the temperature difference between indoors and outdoors.

The thermal transmittance of any structural item such as a wall can be worked out from a knowledge of the physical properties of its component parts. The number of types of structure in use is large, but it is possible to list the transmittance values for a selection of standard walls, floors and ceilings to include the most common types. This has been done for the reader, the resulting heat loss factors appearing in Tables 9, 10, 11 and 12. The last of these gives factors for the one air change per hour ventilation heat loss, computed per square foot of floor area — an expedient to simplify the calculations, as will become clear in a moment. All the tables include the factor for indoor-outdoor temperature difference. Heat loss factors for less common wall and roof constructions can be determined as shown later in this chapter.

We now set out a step-by-step procedure for finding the heat loss of any room.

(1) Measure the area of the windows in the room. Include the window frame in the area.
(2) Measure the area of the outside wall, or walls, of the room. This should be the nett area, excluding windows. Internal partition walls to adjacent rooms are ignored.
(3) Measure the floor area of the room.
(4) Find the appropriate factors for window, wall, floor, ceiling and ventilation losses from Tables 9, 10, 11 and 12.

No difficulty arises with the window and wall factors. The appropriate window or wall construction is found in the left-hand column of Table 9 and the factor is read under the desired room temperature. With floor and ceiling factors we have to consider whether or not there is a heat loss through the surface in question. There will be a floor loss in a ground-floor room and a ceiling loss in an upstairs room (unless of course there are additional upper floors). In a bungalow there will be heat losses through both the floor and the ceiling. The appropriate floor or ceiling construction is found in the left-hand column of Table 10 and Table 11 respectively, and the factor for that particular loss read under the desired room temperature. Ventilation losses are found in the same way, from Table 12. There is no construction to worry about here; merely the room height.

We now have heat loss factors for the room in question for windows, walls, floor (if a ground-floor room), ceiling (if a top-floor room), and ventilation. The last three of these — floor, ceiling and ventilation factors — are now going to be added together. We can do this because they are all based on the floor area of the room in question, the ceiling area being the same as the floor area in most rooms. So we write down steps number 5 to 9:

(5) Add together the floor, ceiling and ventilation factors.

(6) Multiply the window area measured in step 1 by the window loss factor.

(7) Multiply the wall area measured in step 2 by the wall factor.

(8) Multiply the floor area measured in step 3 by the sum of the floor, ceiling and ventilation factors, found in step 5.

(9) Add together the answers of steps 6, 7 and 8. The total is the room heat loss in Btu per hour.

Table 9

Window and wall heat loss factors

REF	Construction	Room temperature		
		60°F	65°F	70°F
	Normal window	30.0	35.0	40.0
	Double glazed window	15.0	17.5	20.0
W1	Corrugated iron, unlined	36.0	42.0	48.0
W13	Corrugated iron, lined ½" insulating fibreboard, joints filled	9.6	11.2	12.8
W2	Corrugated asbestos sheet, unlined	34.5	40.3	46.0
W8	Corrugated asbestos sheet, lined ½" asbestos insulating board, joints filled	12.8	14.9	17.0

REF	Construction	Room temperature		
		60°F	65°F	70°F
W5	Timber frame with ¾″ tongued and grooved boards	17.1	20.0	22.8
W3	4½″ brick wall, unplastered	19.2	22.5	25.6
W4	4½″ brick wall, plastered	17.1	20.0	22.8
W7	9″ solid brick wall, plastered	12.9	15.1	17.2
W11	13½″ solid brick wall, plastered	10.5	12.3	14.0
W12	11″ cavity brick wall plastered	9.9	11.6	13.2
W15	4½″ brick, cavity, 3″ breeze block, plastered	8.6	10.0	11.4
W16	4½″ brick, cavity, 3″ aerated concrete block, plastered	8.2	9.6	11.0
W10	8″ clinker concrete, plastered	10.8	12.6	14.4
W14	10″ clinker concrete, plastered	9.3	10.8	12.4
W6	12″ stone wall	15.0	17.5	20.0
W9	18″ stone wall	12.0	14.0	16.0

Table 10

Floor heat loss factors

Construction	Room temperature		
	60°F	65°F	70°F
Wood floors			
Bare boards	9.0	10.5	12.0
With linoleum, rubber or plastic tiles	7.5	8.8	10.0
Carpeted, with felt or sponge rubber underlay	5.4	6.3	7.2
Solid floors			
Uncovered, or with linoleum, rubber or plastic tile covering	5.7	6.7	7.6
With parquet or cork tile covering	5.3	6.1	7.0
Carpeted, with felt or sponge rubber underlay	4.4	5.1	5.8

Table 11

Ceiling and roof heat loss factors

REF	Construction	Room temperature		
		60°F	65°F	70°F
	Glass skylight	36.0	42.0	48.0
	Double glazed skylight	18.0	21.0	24.0

REF	Construction	Room temperature		
		60°F	65°F	70°F
	Pitched roof without ceiling (Factors apply to room floor area, not roof area)			
R1	Corrugated iron, unlined	52.0	60.5	69.0
R7	Corrugated iron, lined 1″ wooden boards	13.2	15.4	17.6
R2	Corrugated asbestos, unlined	48.0	56.5	65.0
R5	Corrugated asbestos, lined ½″ asbestos insulating board	15.3	18.1	20.9
	Pitched roof with ceiling (Factors apply to room floor area, not roof area)			
R3	Plaster ceiling, loft space, tiled roof on battens	16.8	19.6	22.4
R8	Plaster ceiling, loft space, tiled or slated roof on wooden boards with felt	9.0	10.5	12.0
	Flat roof			
R4	Asphalt on 6″ concrete, plastered	16.5	19.2	22.0
R6	Asphalt on 6″ thick hollow tile, plastered	13.2	15.4	17.6
R9	Asphalt on 1¼″ wooden boards, joists and plaster ceiling	9.0	10.5	12.0

Table 12

Ventilation heat loss factors

Room height	Room temperature		
	60°F	65°F	70°F
7ft	4.2	4.9	5.6
8ft	4.8	5.6	6.4
10ft	6.0	7.0	8.0
12ft	7.2	8.4	9.6

Example
What is the heat loss of a ground floor room 15ft × 12ft in size, and 8ft high? There is one outside wall, 15ft long, of brick cavity construction 11in thick, plastered inside. The window measures 6ft × 4ft. The room has a wooden floor which is carpeted, with a felt underlay. The design room temperature is 70°F.

95

The sequence of steps is numbered as before.
(1)   Window area is 24sq ft.
(2)   The gross wall area is 15ft long × 8ft high, ie 120sq ft. We need the nett area, so we deduct the 24sq ft window, leaving 96sq ft.
(3)   The floor area is 15ft × 12ft, ie 180sq ft.
(4)   From Table 9 the factor for a normal window in a 70° room is 40.0.
      Also from Table 9 the factor for an 11in plastered cavity brick wall in a 70° room is 13.2.
      From Table 10 the factor for a carpeted wooden floor, with felt underlay, in a 70° room is 7.2.
      The room is on the ground floor, so there will be no ceiling heat loss.
      From Table 12 the ventilation factor for an 8ft high room at 70° is 6.4.
(5)   Adding together the floor, ceiling and ventilation factors, we have 7.2 + 0 + 6.4 = 13.6
(6)   Window loss: 24sq ft × 40.0 =   960Btu/h
(7)   Wall loss: 96sq ft × 13.2 = 1,270Btu/h
(8)   Other losses: 180sq ft × 13.6 = 2,450Btu/h
(9)   Adding the answers to steps 6, 7 and 8, we get 4,680Btu/h.

That is the total heat loss of the room. It can be converted into kilowatts if desired with the aid of the conversion chart on page 114. It will be noticed that the answers to steps 7 and 8 have been rounded to the nearest ten. There is no point in aiming for greater accuracy than this. The data on which heat losses are based are not sufficiently precise to justify the attempt. The various losses could be rounded to the nearest hundred without serious error. The thermal conductance of a wall for instance will vary with the amount of moisture it holds, and this varies with the weather. One air change per hour is taken as the room ventilation rate, but a high wind can affect the rate considerably. The tabulated factors have been computed for average winter conditions and, except on very exposed sites, will be found satisfactory in practice.

Other Constructions

There are so many materials available for the construction of composite walls and roofs that it would be impossible to list all the combinations. The alignment chart of Fig 14 has been prepared to meet the difficulty. It shows the effect of adding insulating or structural material to the walls and roofs listed in Tables 9 and 11. The basic wall and roof constructions are marked on the left-hand vertical line, using the reference numbers from Tables 9 and 11, and the additional insulating or other material is marked along the base line. A straight-edge joining any point on the vertical to any point on the base line will cut the slanting middle line at a point representing the heat loss factor for the total combination of materials selected. The heat loss factors are given for rooms at 60° and 70°. The factor for a room at 65° may be found by averaging the two given factors.

Example
A 9in plastered solid brick wall is insulated by the addition of ½in fibreboard, nailed to battens on the wall. The room design temperature is 70°. What will be the heat loss factor for the improved wall?
The battens provide an air gap. The reference for the basic wall is W7 from Table 9. Using Fig 14, a straight line joining the point W7 with the point for ½in fibreboard plus air gap cuts the slanting line at the value 8.7 for a 70° room. 8.7 is the required heat loss factor.

We see from Table 9 that the untreated wall had a heat loss factor of 17.2, so the addition of the insulation has virtually halved the heat loss through the wall. The effect of adding insulation to an existing structure is obviously of great importance. It is dealt with in detail in Chapter 10.

The chart of Fig 14 can be used to determine the effect of multiple additions of insulation or other material. Fig 15 shows the procedure. After the operation already described, if instead of reading off the heat

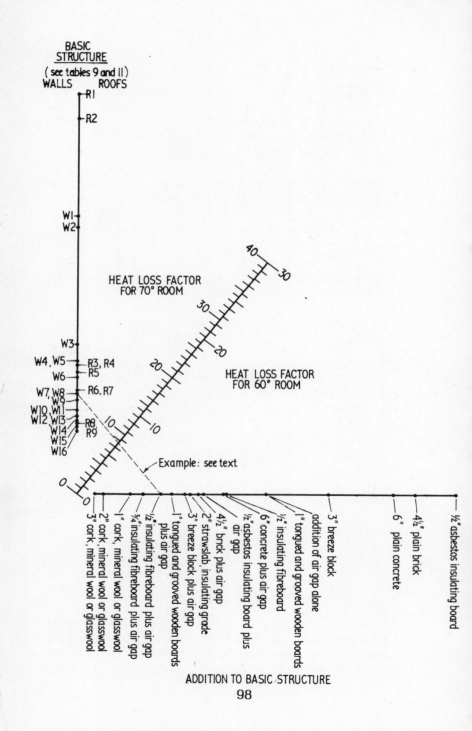

BASIC
STRUCTURE
(see tables 9 and 11)
WALLS   ROOFS

R1
R2

W1
W2

HEAT LOSS FACTOR
FOR 70° ROOM

40
30
30
20
20
10
10

W3
W4, W5 — R3, R4
W6 — R5
W7, W8 — R6, R7
W9
W10, W11
W12, W13
W14 — R8
W15   R9
W16

HEAT LOSS FACTOR
FOR 60° ROOM

Example: see text

0
0

3" cork, mineral wool or glasswool
2" cork, mineral wool or glasswool
1" cork, mineral wool or glasswool
¾" insulating fibreboard plus air gap
½" insulating fibreboard plus air gap
1" tongued and grooved wooden boards plus air gap
3" breeze block plus air gap
2" strawslab insulating grade
4½" brick plus air gap
½" asbestos insulating board plus air gap
6" concrete plus air gap
½" insulating fibreboard
1" tongued and grooved wooden boards
addition of air gap alone
3" breeze block
6" plain concrete
4½" plain brick
½" asbestos insulating board

ADDITION TO BASIC STRUCTURE
98

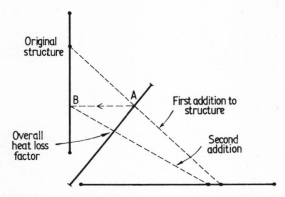

Fig 15 Effect on heat loss factor of multiple additions to structure   The chart of Fig 14 can be used to find the effect of several separate additions to the basic wall or roof. The procedure is shown here

loss factor from the slanting line (point A in Fig 15) a point is marked on the left-hand vertical immediately opposite A (shown as B in Fig 15), then B represents the new basic structure, and the process may be repeated for a second addition to the wall or roof. The procedure may be repeated again for a third addition to the structure, and so on.

It will be appreciated that the heat loss factor for virtually any combination of materials can be determined in this way.

Fig 14 Heat loss factors for composite walls and roofs   A straight line joining the appropriate points shows the effect on the heat loss factor of adding insulation or structural material to the basic walls and roofs listed in Tables 9 and 11

Chapter 9

Sizing the Plant

Having determined how much heat each room will need, we are now in a position to specify, if we wish, the output required from each room heater and the rating of the central plant. Alternatively the information we have will enable us to check a contractor's tender and specification.

Pipe Emission

With a wet system the room heat loss must be met by the combined emission of the room heater, whatever it may be, and the heating pipes which run through the room. The pipes are dealt with first. The route they follow is not determined until the proposed scheme is set out on a drawing. If such a drawing is available then the length of pipe in each room may be measured from it. If not, a possible arrangement can be visualised or sketched, and the pipe length estimated. The final requirement for the room-heater output will not be seriously affected by changes in the conjectured run.

The heat emission from pipes is affected by a number of factors, one being the pipe diameter. A single pipe system has on average larger pipes than a two-pipe system. This fact enables us, without knowing the type of system, to estimate the emission closely enough for our present purpose. We multiply the run of pipe in the room (measured in feet) by the average emission factor 60 (a suitable approximation for a domestic system), ignoring whether the pipe is single or double. This will give a conservative estimate in Btu per hour of the heat emission we can expect. We deduct this emission from the calculated room heat loss. The balance of the heat needed must come from the room heater.

Room Heaters for Wet Systems—General Information

As every manufacturer has his own design of heater it is impossible to specify the physical size of the room heaters for given outputs, except in the case of panel radiators. The basic design of these is common to all makes. They are so widely used that a chart showing the size, in square feet of heating surface for any output, is well worth including here (Fig 16). There are some special designs which incorporate fins at the rear. For these only the makers' catalogue will give the correct size, as the overall heat emission per square foot will be very different from that of the conventional panel radiator.

Room heaters other than radiators can be specified by required output and room air temperature.

With low temperature embedded panel systems the heat emission depends on both room air temperature and mean radiant temperature. The heat transfer by conduction from the embedded pipes to the panel surface must also be calculated. It is emphasised once again that the design and specification of a panel heating system should only be entrusted to those experienced in it and with a knowledge of the principles involved.

Panel Radiators

Radiator sizes are quoted in square feet of heating surface. As radiators are produced in a number of heights and with one or multiple panels, the area of heating surface is only one part of the specification. The height is usually chosen so that the radiator will not protrude above a window sill, allowing for the necessary floor clearance of about 6in at the bottom. The number of panels is determined by considerations of length. Wherever possible single panel radiators are chosen. They look better and they have a greater heat emission per square foot than the double panel type. This comes about because the two inner faces of the latter, opposite to each other, cannot radiate heat to the room, but only convect. However, if a single panel model of the chosen height would be inordinately long for the required heat output then a double panel one must be used. Despite its lower rate of emission per square foot, and consequently greater heating surface, it will be shorter in length than the single panel alternative.

The alignment chart of Fig 16 gives the heating surface needed for any output for both single and double panel radiators. A straight-edge joining the heat output line on the left to the radiator and room temperature line on the right will cut the centre line at a point showing the heating surface needed. For each room it is best to jot down the two alternative heating surface figures — for single or double panel — so that the procedure will not have to be repeated if a double panel model proves necessary. The right-hand line is calibrated for a range of radiator temperatures. This has been done so that the chart can be used to size radiators throughout a single pipe system. For these, radiators at the beginning of the circuit will have a mean temperature of 170°F, those in the middle, 160°, and those at the end, 150°. For two-pipe systems a mean radiator temperature of 170° is used throughout, as indicated on the chart. The two room temperatures need no explanation. For 65° rooms the two scale positions may be averaged.

Radiator heights are standardised (within about 1in) at 12in, 18in, 24in and 30in. If the reader has access to a manufacturer's catalogue the required heating surface will be found listed under the chosen height, together with the length of the radiator, for both single and double panel types. If a single panel version would extend well beyond the width of the window below which it is to be installed, the double panel alternative

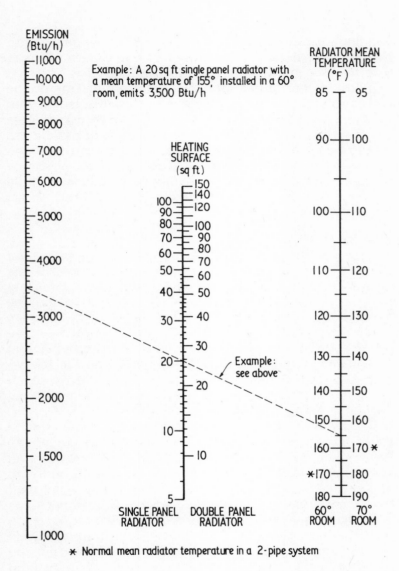

EMISSION
(Btu/h)

Example: A 20 sq ft single panel radiator with a mean temperature of 155° installed in a 60° room, emits 3,500 Btu/h

RADIATOR MEAN
TEMPERATURE
(°F)

HEATING
SURFACE
(sq ft)

Example:
see above

SINGLE PANEL
RADIATOR

DOUBLE PANEL
RADIATOR

60°
ROOM

70°
ROOM

✳ Normal mean radiator temperature in a 2-pipe system

Fig 16 Heat emission from panel radiators   A straight line across the chart will show the heat output of a single or double panel radiator for any radiator temperature. For a room temperature of 65°, the two room temperature scales may be averaged

103

will look better and should be chosen. Other length restrictions, including those tabulated in Chapter 6, may lead to the choice of the double panel model.

If the reader has no catalogue, the radiator may still be specified — by height, maximum acceptable length and alternative heating surface areas for single or double panel, with the instruction that single panel radiators should be used wherever possible.

If Fig 16 is used to check on a tender already received, the contractor's specification ought to include the type and heating surface of each radiator, so no difficulty should arise.

The Boiler Rating

The boiler must be capable of meeting the total heat losses of the house plus the heat requirements of the domestic hot water. However, it must have a margin over and above this total so that the system can be operated intermittently, ie turned off at night, to save fuel. When the heating is off, the structure of the house cools. This loss of heat from the structure has to be replaced during the heating-up period on the following day and, if the period is to be kept reasonably short, the boiler must have quite a substantial margin over the normal running heat loss of the house.

It may be argued that as the structure has to be reheated on the following day, nothing is gained by turning off the heating overnight. A little thought will show the error of this. Consider the wall of a building. The rate of heat loss to outside is less from a cool wall than from a warm one, simply because the temperature difference between the wall and the outside air is less in the first case. Now, no matter how long the preheating period in the morning, the amount of heat put into the structure will not exceed that which was lost by it in cooling. It must in fact be an identical amount. And this in turn is less than the amount that would be lost if the wall were maintained at full working temperature throughout the night, because a warm wall loses more heat than a cool one.

Intermittent heating then is worthwhile. The saving to be achieved by it will depend on how quickly the morning preheating can be done, because the shorter this period is, the less the total amount of heat transmitted *through* the structure during the heating-up. For quick preheating, the spare boiler capacity must be substantial. A reasonable margin is 25 per cent of the total heat losses of the house. Larger margins will give a quicker heat up, but will mean a bigger boiler.

Heat losses have already been dealt with in Chapter 8, so all that remains is to assess the heat needed for domestic hot water. That depends on the size of the cylinder and on an acceptable time for heating the contents from cold. A cylinder capacity of 7 or 8gal for each person in the household is normal (with a minimum of 25gal), and a heating-up time of 2½hr. The heat requirement of a 30gal cylinder is on this basis 13,000Btu/h, including an allowance for heat loss from the primary mains between boiler and cylinder. Heat requirements for larger and smaller cylinders will be roughly in proportion. A house with a design heat loss of 40,000Btu/h (and therefore 50,000Btu/h including the preheating margin), and with a 30gal hot water cylinder, should have a boiler of about 63,000Btu/h capacity.

Where there are extensive runs of pipe not providing useful heat — and such pipes must of course be insulated — the heat loss from them must be included in the boiler rating. The most usual example of this is where pipes are run in the roof space. A heat emission of 20Btu/h for each foot run of insulated pipe is a reasonable allowance.

If the controls are arranged so that the hot water cylinder cannot take heat from the boiler during the early morning preheating time, then the hot water allowance can be omitted from the total boiler capacity — at least in part. The boiler must in that case be sized to meet whichever is larger — the total heat loss plus the preheat margin, or the total heat loss plus the hot water load. There will still be times when this second load has to be met.

Warm Air Systems

It is not suggested that the would-be purchaser design his own warm air heating system, any more than he should a wet system. However, if he wishes to check the adequacy of a proposed warm air scheme, he will need to work out heat losses, as shown in Chapter 8, and also to make an assessment of the air flow rate to each room.

The flow rate needed to meet a room's heat losses will depend on the air delivery temperature from the heater. The hotter the air the smaller the rate of flow — and, incidentally, the greater the possibility of patchy heating and excessive temperature gradients in the room. Heat losses from ducts are greater with high air temperatures. An addition must be made to the calculated room heat loss to cover duct heat emission in any case. The duct surface area (in square feet) should be multiplied by 100 for uninsulated sheet metal, or by 30 for insulated ducts. For instance a 12in × 6in duct will have a surface area of 3sq ft for every foot of its length. If it is 6ft long, the total area will be 18sq ft and the heat loss will work out at 1,800Btu/h if it is bare, or 540Btu/h if insulated — as it should be. These figures are only approximate, of course, but they will do. Duct runs for domestic heating are usually short, so we can use rules of thumb which would not be acceptable for a large installation.

The duct heat loss must be added to the room heat loss already calculated. The quantity of air to be delivered to the room will be based on this augmented figure. The procedure ensures that each room will have enough air to meet its own heat loss even though the air has dropped in temperature in transit. A main duct

---

Fig 17 Air flow rates for warm air heating A straight line across the chart will show the necessary air flow rate for any room heat requirement and any supply air temperature. For a room temperature of 65°, the two room temperature scales may be averaged

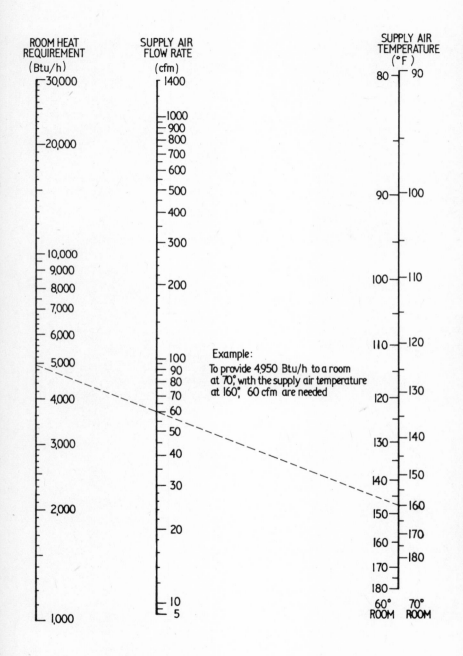

ROOM HEAT
REQUIREMENT
(Btu/h)

SUPPLY AIR
FLOW RATE
(cfm)

SUPPLY AIR
TEMPERATURE
(°F)

Example:
To provide 4,950 Btu/h to a room
at 70°, with the supply air temperature
at 160°, 60 cfm are needed

60°
ROOM

70°
ROOM

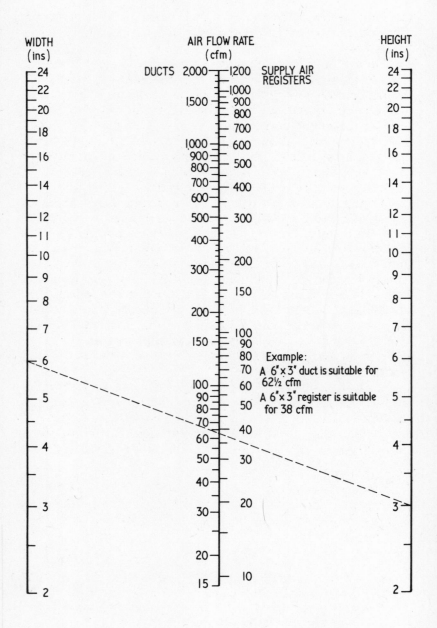

WIDTH
(ins)

AIR FLOW RATE
(cfm)

HEIGHT
(ins)

DUCTS

SUPPLY AIR
REGISTERS

Example:
A 6" x 3" duct is suitable for 62½ cfm

A 6" x 3" register is suitable for 38 cfm

serving two or more rooms should have its heat emission divided between the rooms in rough proportion to the room heat losses.

The air flow rate for each room can be read from Fig 17. A straight-edge joining the augmented heat loss figure on the left with the delivery temperature (as it leaves the central unit) on the right will cut the centre line at the required air input rate to the room, in cubic feet per minute. Although the air flow rate is specified on a minute's flow, the heat loss figure is in Btu per hour, as calculated in Chapter 8. The calibration of the chart takes care of the time difference.

Having established the required air flow to each room, we can check the proposed duct size from Fig 18. A straight-edge joining the duct width on one side of the chart with the duct height on the other will cross the centre line at an air flow rate suitable for that size of duct. If the air flow rate for the room in question exceeds this figure the proposed duct is too small. The centre line of the chart is marked with two scales of air flow rate. That on the left is for ducts, and that on the right for supply registers. Supply registers need to be larger than ducts for a given air flow rate. The chart can be used for either.

Main ducts serving several rooms have to carry the air supply for all of those rooms. The air flow rates can be totalled from the various outlets back to the central unit. The duct sizes for these are checked in the same way, from Fig 18, as those for individual rooms.

Example
A room with a heat loss of 4,500Btu/h is heated by warm air. The room temperature is 70°F and the air leaves the central unit at 160°. The proposed 6in × 3in

---

Fig 18 Warm air heating duct and supply register sizes A straight line across the chart will show the air carrying capacity of any rectangular duct or supply register up to 24in in size. The chart is suitable for domestic installations only

insulated supply duct is run direct from the heater outlet to the room, a distance of 10ft. Is the duct size adequate?

We first work out the duct heat loss. A 6in × 3in duct has a girth of 18in, or 1½ft. So the duct surface area for the 10ft run is 10ft × 1½ft = 15sq ft. The heat emission is therefore 15 × 30 = 450Btu/h.

This must be added to the room heat loss of 4,500Btu/h, making 4,950Btu/h in all.

Using Fig 17, a straight line joining 4,950Btu/h on the left with a delivery air temperature of 160° (serving a 70° room) cuts the middle line at 60cfm (cubic feet per minute). This is the required air flow to the room.

Turning to Fig 18, and joining the 6in width on the left-hand side with the 3in height on the right, we find the straight-edge cuts the centre line at 62½cfm. The 6in × 3in duct is suitable for this flow rate, and so is also suitable for the smaller rate of 60cfm that we need.

The central warm air unit must be capable of meeting the total of the room heat losses and the duct losses. It should have a margin above this total to permit inter-mittent operation. With the method of control and the supply air temperatures customary with this form of heating, the preheating period will not be shortened by increasing the overload margin much above 25 per cent, so this may be taken as a suitable allowance.

This matter of the availability of the central plant capacity is an important one, and worth a moment's attention.

Central Plant Capacity and Availability

We have seen that fuel may be saved by intermittent heating and that the shorter the morning preheating period the more the saving will be. Short preheating periods are achieved by high heating capacity in the central plant — higher than is needed to meet the steady state heat loss from the building. However, central plant heating capacity is no good if it cannot be used, and the system of heating controls normally employed is such that there is in fact a limit on the rate at which heat can be emitted into the rooms. The limit for wet systems is very different from that for warm air ones, as we shall see.

A radiator or convector installation is designed to operate with a boiler flow temperature of about 180°F and a return temperature of 160°. The boiler thermostat controls the flow temperature at all times. The setting may be raised if necessary to boost output (assuming the boiler and burner have the heating surface and fuel-burning capacity) but for the present purpose we may ignore this and assume normal conditions with the thermostat set at 180°. In cold weather the water flows to the radiators at 180° and leaves them at 160°, the radiator having the mean temperature of 170°. The room at 70° is 100° cooler than the radiator. With this temperature difference the radiator emits heat at a steady rate. To fix our ideas let us put a figure to this and call it 5,000Btu/h.

Now let us consider what happens during the morning preheating period. We shall assume the boiler has a large margin of heating capacity over the design heat loss requirement. The time switch starts the system at perhaps 4 or 5 o'clock. The rooms have cooled overnight and the air in them is at 40°. The outside air is at 30°. The walls of the room have cooled, the outside ones to well below room temperature. The heating pump starts, the burner fires, and water at 40° is pumped into the boiler from the cold heating system. The boiler, working at full capacity, manages to produce a flow temperature of perhaps 80°. Note that this rate of working is double the boiler's normal rate. It is heating the circulated quantity of water through 40° instead of the usual 20°.

The water at 80° is delivered to the radiators to replace the water at 40° that was standing in them. The mean radiator temperature is, for the moment, 60°. The heat emission from the radiator to the room will be about one-eighth of the normal output. (The emission is

111

not strictly proportional to the difference between radiator and room temperatures.) So we have the boiler working at twice its normal rate and only one-eighth of the normal output coming into the rooms. The remainder is of course going to heat up the water and metal in the system.

The boiler flow temperature rises rapidly. The room temperature also rises, but much more slowly. When the radiator is 100° warmer than the room, the emission will be at the normal design rate of 5,000Btu/h. But this will occur when the room temperature is still in the forties. As the radiator and room temperatures continue to rise, the difference between them becomes much wider than the normal 100°, and the output to the room consequently much higher than 5,000Btu/h. The capacity of the boiler is being used to the full, and the boiler thermostat still has not reached the burner cut-off temperature of 180°. The 100 per cent overload margin of the boiler is fully available to the system.

Now consider what happens in a warm air system, with the supply air temperature controlled at 165° and the return air normally at 65° — from rooms at 70°, 65° and 60°. Under similar conditions to those already considered the heater starts with the rooms at 40°. This will be the initial return air temperature. In heating the air to 165° the unit will be working at 25 per cent greater output than normal, warming the air through 125° instead of 100°. As the room warms up and the return air temperature rises, the range through which the unit can heat the return air will constantly diminish. It will not deliver air at a higher temperature than 165° because the control thermostat will not permit it to do so. It will cut the burner output at any higher delivery temperature. The maximum overload margin that the system can use is therefore 25 per cent. No matter how powerful the burner, any heater capacity above this amount is unavailable to the system.

The warm air installation has the advantage that there is no mass of metal and water to be heated; what heat it does produce goes directly to the rooms. But the limit on overload capacity remains. Before we leave this matter it may be remarked that a warm air system using a lower delivery air temperature than that considered will not be limited to the same extent. If the delivery air is controlled at eg 115°, the effect of dropping the return temperature from the daytime 65° to the early morning 40° is to increase the potential heating range from 50° to 75°, giving a maximum usable overload margin of 50 per cent.

Electric Systems

Electric warm air systems which have a control on delivery air temperature, fall into the same category as those considered in the previous section in terms of availability of output.

An off-peak storage system of any kind will have a rating which will depend on the intended charging times. It must be able to store sufficient heat between charges to deliver the maximum output until the next charging period starts. Originally, when simple overnight charging was used, the rating of the heater elements was calculated on the ratio of the full day length of twenty-four hours to the overnight charge time of, say, eight hours. A system which was required to deliver 5kW would therefore have been charged at a rate of 15kW overnight. This method of sizing, being based on twenty-four hour operation at full output, gives an inherent reserve charge (within the limitations considered in the previous section) for intermittent use.

With some systems — electric floor warming for example — intermittent use is not possible. For the others the advent of 'White Meter' tariffs has complicated matters because heaters are now sometimes sized to receive some of their charge during the day. This is done presumably to keep the bulk and weight of the storage medium to a minimum. The effect for the purchaser is that he will not only have to pay normal day rates for part of his heating, he may well find that the system is designed to operate continuously rather

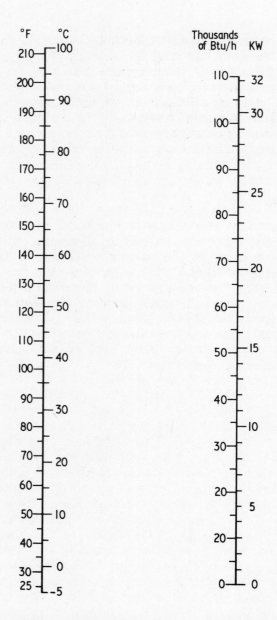

Fig 19 Conversion scale of temperature, and the electrical
equivalent of heat

114

than intermittently, with the additional running cost that that will entail.

As for the sizing of the central unit, that will depend on what proportion of the design load is to be met by overnight charging. Where the purchaser has a choice he would do best to insist on having the maximum possible overnight charge and, along with it, a time switch control that will permit intermittent operation of the system as a whole. He should then be able to work the system intermittently through part of the winter at least.

Direct electric heaters lead to no such difficulty. The electric loading equivalent to the room heat loss can be read from Fig 19. This type of heater is usually produced in a range of standard sizes so, by choosing the rating next above the room heat loss, one automatically gets an overload margin. If they are to be used as the main source of house heating the units can be controlled by a time switch, though the high temperature radiant heaters in this category are, of course, designed to produce comfort at short notice and are most economically used in that way.

Chapter 10

Thermal Insulation

If one face of a slab of solid material is maintained at a higher temperature than the opposite face, heat will flow through the slab from the warmer to the cooler side. Such heat flow through the body of the material is by thermal conduction, that is by minute vibrations of the molecules of which the body is composed. The rate of heat flow will depend on the temperature difference between the warm and cool faces and on the thickness of the material between the faces. The rate also varies greatly from one material to another. For instance the rate of heat flow through a sheet of aluminium is almost 5,000 times as great as through a sheet of cork of the same thickness, with a similar temperature difference across both substances. If we are looking for an insulant to impede the flow of heat, cork is obviously a suitable material and aluminium is not.

The materials used in building construction are chosen primarily for their strength and cheapness. Unfortunately those materials which best meet these criteria are not often very satisfactory from the point of view of heat conservation. Some traditional building materials were much better in this respect than modern ones. A cottage with thick brick or rubble-filled stone walls, and with a thatched roof, had excellent thermal properties, being warm in winter and cool in summer. Its small windows were equally an asset from this point of view, though not suited to the more recent desire for light.

With a modern building, if we wish to reduce heat losses we must add insulation to the structure. This can be done either during the building process or after it is complete. There are now statutory requirements governing the thermal transmittance of walls and roofs in new buildings. The regulations are not particularly demanding and, with the prospect of recurring fuel crises, they are likely to be made more stringent in the future. There is scope for this. British houses are probably less well insulated than any others in northern Europe or America.

The Benefits of Insulation

The beneficial effects of insulating a building are threefold. In the first place the insulation reduces the flow of heat through the structure to outside, thereby reducing the heat requirement of each of the rooms. Secondly, the insulation raises the inside surface temperature to a higher level, thus raising the mean radiant temperature of the rooms, and so producing equivalent comfort at a lower room air temperature. Thirdly, if the insulation is applied to the inside of the walls and roof, as it usually is, the effect is to quicken the response of the building to changes in output of the heating system. This is because, when the inside face is insulated, the main mass of the structure is heated and cooled through a smaller range of temperature than it otherwise would be. This also means a shorter heating-up period at the beginning of the day.

All the benefits promote fuel economy; the second one conduces to personal comfort also. If the insulating work is carried out in conjunction with the installation of central heating, the heating system will be smaller than it otherwise would be, with a saving in capital cost as well.

Insulating Materials

There are so many kinds of thermal insulation on the market that it would be impossible to list them all. Most are of lightweight material, depending on the presence of trapped air to form a heat barrier. Free air can be used to transfer heat by convection. Still air, however, is a poor conductor of heat. Trapped in the fibres of the insulation, it adds enormously to the thermal resistance of the enclosing material. Glass provides an example. Ordinary glass is not a good insulant. It has a thermal conductivity of 7.3 units. That means that 1sq ft of glass 1in thick will conduct 7.3Btu per hour for every degree of temperature by which one face is warmer than the other. Glass wool, a commonly used insulant consisting of nothing but finely spun filaments of glass with air trapped between them, has a thermal conductivity of 0.23. That means that 1sq ft of glass wool 1in thick will conduct less than one-thirtieth of the heat that the solid glass would conduct under similar conditions. The glass wool is about one-fiftieth of the weight of the solid sheet.

Glass wool insulation is available in the form of mats, quilts, blankets and cylindrical rigid sections for pipework. Mineral wool, which has similar thermal properties to glass wool and is rather more pleasant to handle, comes in most of the same forms and also as granules which can be used to insulate top floor ceilings by filling the space between floor joists in the loft. Another use of mineral wool is to fill the air gap of cavity brick walls, creating a multiple air gap which reduces the heat loss through the wall by about two-thirds. An alternative insulant for this purpose is a special plastic foam. The insulating property of the foam is a little less than that of the mineral wool. In both cases the material is pumped into the cavity from outside, a brick being removed from a section of wall for the purpose. The filling must of course be waterproof and resistant to water penetration by capillary action. One manufacturer, specialising in this work, offers a twenty-year guarantee.

Plastic insulation is available in a variety of forms, including granules for upper floor ceiling insulation as with mineral wool, but also in blocks or sheets which are easily cut to shape and can be used for ceiling or wall insulation in combination with a building board or plasterboard finish.

There are a number of insulating boards, some based on wood, some on paper, straw, flax or asbestos. An advantage that inorganic or synthetic materials such as glass wool, mineral wool, asbestos and plastics have over natural organic materials, is that they are virtually rot-proof. This is only of consequence where there is a risk of damp.

Insulating board is often available in two forms — either plain or with one face covered with aluminium foil. Aluminium is a good conductor of heat, so the foil does nothing to reduce the conductivity of the board. What it does is to reduce thermal radiation across any air gap bounded by the foil-coated face. Polished metal is a fine reflector but a poor radiator of heat, and also a poor absorber of radiation. Where foil-coated board is used, the metal face must therefore be adjacent to an air gap for the board to produce the maximum insulating effect. The foil will also act as a moisture barrier, whether it bounds an air gap or not.

Windows

Windows in a normally exposed position have an overall thermal transmittance of 1Btu/ft²h°F, which is to say each square foot of window will transmit one heat unit per hour for every degree of temperature by which the room air is warmer than outdoors. This is three or four times the transmittance of most uninsulated walls. Windows therefore make a significant contribution to heat loss. The only way in which they can be insulated is by double glazing. This will halve the heat loss. Triple glazing will reduce it to one-third, and so on. Multiple glazing, beyond two panes, is progressively more expensive per layer and, at present costs, probably not justifiable.

Surface Resistances

The reader may have noticed that although glass was said a little way back to have a thermal conductivity of

119

7.3 units for a full inch thickness, the overall thermal transmittance of a window only ⅛in thick is as little as 1 unit. This may appear to contradict the commonsense assumption that a thin sheet of glass will transmit more heat than a thick one. That commonsense assumption is in fact right, but there is no contradiction. The apparent anomaly arises merely from the definitions of thermal conductivity and thermal transmittance.

Conductivity is a measure of the heat flow rate through a 1in thickness of solid material when one face is 1°F warmer that the opposite face, whereas the overall thermal transmittance gives the heat flow rate when the general air temperature on one side of the window, or other structure, is 1°F warmer than the air on the other side. The rate of heat flow in the first case is very much greater than in the second. It will pay us to see why.

When heat is transmitted through a structural element such as a wall or a window, the rate of heat flow will depend on the difference in temperature of the air on the two sides of the structure, and also on the thermal resistance of the material. The higher the resistance the smaller the heat flow. The thermal resistance is built up of several parts. In the case of any simple solid element, such as a window pane, there are three parts. There is the resistance to heat flow of the glass itself, there is the resistance of a thin stagnant layer of air on the room side of the glass, and there is the resistance of a similar but even thinner stagnant air layer on the outside of the glass. Still air, as we know, is a poor conductor of heat. So these surface resistances, as they are called, are never negligible. In the case of a window they make up almost the whole of the resistance to heat flow.

If the air in a room is at 70°F and the air outside is at 30°, there is clearly a 40° temperature difference across the window from inside to out. The internal surface resistance of the window (the resistance of the air film) is so high that there is a temperature drop of 28° between the air in the room and the inside face of the window pane. The glass temperature will therefore be 42°. It will feel cold to the touch. The resistance of the window pane itself can be worked out from the thermal conductivity of 7.3 units given earlier. It produces a temperature drop from one face of the glass to the other of 0.69°, that is considerably less than one degree. The remaining temperature drop of just over 11° takes place across the outside surface air layer. So the 40° temperature difference between the room air and the outside is built up of the three temperature drops: 28°, 1° say, and 11°. As the same rate of heat flow is taking place through all successive components of the window, the temperature drop through any part is proportional to the resistance of that part. We see that the resistance to heat flow of the actual glass of the window is less than one-fortieth part of the total resistance. This accounts for the apparent discrepancy between the thermal conductivity of glass (measured between its two faces) and the thermal transmittance of the window (including the effect of the two surface resistances).

We have looked at this matter at some length because the effect of surface resistances can never be neglected in heat flow calculations. The inside surface resistance of a wall produces a temperature drop between room air and wall surface, just as with a window. This occurs only when there is heat flow through the wall, of course. Where there is no heat flow there is no temperature drop. For instance an internal partition wall with a heated room on the far side will have a surface temperature at room air temperature level. The determination of the mean radiant temperature of a room involves the calculation of the temperatures of all the room surfaces, an operation which would be impossible without a knowledge of the surface resistances.

Air Gaps

The important point, for our present purpose, is the effect that surface resistances have on insulation against heat loss. The reason that double glazing halves the heat loss through a window is that the additional pane of glass doubles the number of surface resistances from two to four. The glass itself has a negligible effect, as we have seen. Similarly if an air gap can be introduced into a wall or ceiling without otherwise altering the existing structure, the thermal transmittance of the wall or ceiling will be reduced. The improvement will not generally be so marked as with a single glazed window. That can only be the case when the thermal resistance of the structure lies almost wholly in the surface films, and most walls do not fall into that category. However, when insulation is to be added to a wall or roof, there are usually a number of ways in which the job can be done, and including an air gap may not be difficult. It will certainly improve the insulation effect. Such a gap should not be too wide, or internal convection will reduce its effectiveness; nor too narrow, or the internal air surface films will overlap. Air gaps of between ½in and 1½in are satisfactory.

Frost Damaged Walls

Insulation is usually added to the inside of a wall rather than the outside. It is cheaper, more easily applied, and produces the additional benefit already described. However, where a wall has suffered frost damage, showing cracks or splits, insulation — which must then of course be of a suitable material to withstand the weather — should only be added externally.

The reason is as follows. Warm air can hold more moisture, in the form of water vapour, than cold air can. The vapour pressure of a mixture of air and water vapour is a measure of the amount of moisture present. Water vapour will move through a permeable barrier, such as a wall, from a region of high vapour pressure to one of low vapour pressure. In a heated house this usually means from inside the wall to outside. If at any point in its migration the vapour reaches a temperature at which it can no longer exist as a vapour (the dew point temperature) it will condense into water. From that point outwards — assuming the temperature continues to drop towards the outside — the wall will hold condensed moisture.

A wall may also contain moisture caused by rising damp, where there is no damp-proof course, or by heavy rain. In very cold weather, if there is moisture in that part of the wall which is at freezing temperature, the moisture will freeze if the conditions last long enough. Insulation applied internally to such a wall, by dropping the temperature of its outer layers, increases the possibility of freezing. External insulation raises the whole wall temperature, reducing the tendency to freeze.

To prevent vapour migration a vapour seal can be included in the insulation, which may then be applied to the inside of the wall. This will not help, of course, where the moisture causing frost damage comes from rain or rising damp.

The Saving Versus the Cost

Thermal insulation costs money to install, but saves money on fuel bills. How do we work out the nett benefit to the house owner?

The fuel saving will depend on the number of therms of heat saved over an average season and on the cost of fuel per useful therm. To determine the amount of heat saved we must find the effect of adding the proposed insulation in terms of reduction of hourly heat loss per square foot of building surface, then multiply this reduction by the area to be insulated and also by the number of hours of heating in the season. The reduction in heat loss must be based on the average winter temperature, not the basic design temperature of 30°F.

All this may seem rather a daunting procedure. However, of the factors mentioned, only two cannot be pre-calculated and incorporated in a table and a chart. These two, which must be left to the reader, are the number of square feet he wishes to insulate and the price he pays

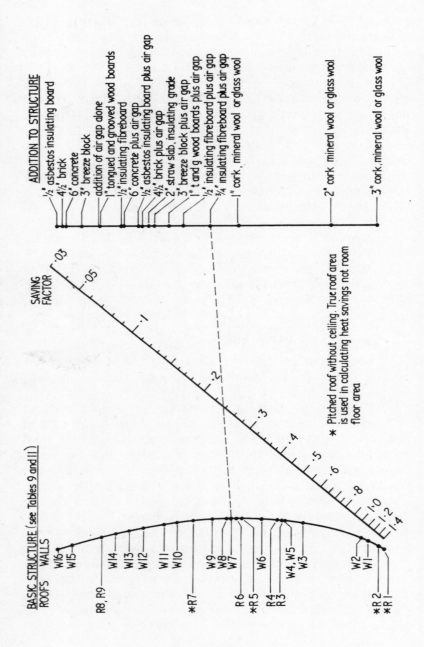

ADDITION TO STRUCTURE

- ½" asbestos insulating board
- 4½" brick
- 6" concrete
- 3" breeze block
- addition of air gap alone
- 1" tongued and grooved wood boards
- ½" insulating fibreboard
- 6" concrete plus air gap
- ½" asbestos insulating board plus air gap
- 4½" brick plus air gap
- 2" straw slab, insulating grade
- 3" breeze block plus air gap
- 1" t and g wood boards plus air gap
- ½" insulating fibreboard plus air gap
- ¾" insulating fibreboard plus air gap
- 1" cork, mineral wool or glass wool
- 2" cork, mineral wool or glass wool
- 3" cork, mineral wool or glass wool

SAVING FACTOR

.03 .05 .1 .2 .3 .4 .5 .6 .8 1.0 1.2 1.4

* Pitched roof without ceiling. True roof area is used in calculating heat savings not room floor area

BASIC STRUCTURE (see Tables 9 and 11)

ROOFS   WALLS

- W16
- W15
- R8, R9
- W14
- W13
- W12
- W11
- W10
- *R7
- W9
- W8
- W7
- R6
- *R5
- W6
- R4
- R3
- W4, W5
- W3
- W2
- W1
- *R2
- *R1

124

for his fuel. For the rest he need only read one factor from the Heat Saving Chart (Fig 20) and extract a second factor from the Annual Use Table (Table 13). The two factors are multiplied together and by the area to be insulated, to give the annual heat saving in therms. The cost of fuel per useful therm may be read from Fig 6, p 54, as was done in Chapter 5. The annual heat saving and the cost of heat per useful therm together give the money saved per year. The example given below will illustrate the procedure.

The Heat Saving Chart consists of three lines. The first is marked at various points along its length with typical wall and roof constructions. These are the basic constructions listed in Tables 9–11, with the same reference numbers. The second (slanting) line is marked with a scale of numbers — the fuel saving factors we are looking for. The third line is marked with various types and thicknesses of insulation. A straight-edge joining the appropriate wall or roof construction to any selected insulation will cut the middle line at a point giving the saving factor for that particular combination of structure and added insulation.

Example
What will be the saving factor for a 9in brick wall, plastered internally, if it is lined with ¾in thick fibreboard, including an air gap?

This is the example illustrated by the light broken line on the chart (Fig 20). It joins the point for a 9in brick wall with that for ¾in fibreboard plus air gap, and crosses the middle line at the value 0.235. That is the required heat saving factor.

To determine the annual saving we must multiply the saving factor by the number of square feet of wall or

Fig 20 Heat saving by insulation   A straight line joining the basic wall or roof construction with the added insulation will cut the middle line at the heat saving factor. This, multiplied by the use factor from Table 13, gives the amount of heat saved annually by the insulation

ceiling to be insulated and by a 'use factor' from Table 13. This last figure allows for the room temperature, the average outdoor temperature and the number of hours the house will be heated.

Table 13

Heat saving by insulation—annual use factors
(to be used in conjunction with Fig 20)

Heating programme	Room temperature		
	60°F	65°F	70°F
System in use all day, every day, but off at night	0.60	0.70	0.80
System in use morning and evening only during the week, all day at weekends, but off every night	0.40	0.46	0.52

Suppose in the example given above that the wall surface to be insulated amounts to 500sq ft, and that the rooms in question have a design temperature of 70°, and that heating is continuous through the day but off at night. We find from Table 13 that the use factor for this heating programme and room temperature is 0.80. We now have the three numbers we need: the saving factor of 0.235 from the chart (Fig 20), the insulated area of 500sq ft, and the use factor of 0.80 from Table 13. We multiply these three numbers together. The answer 94 is the annual heat saving in therms.

To find the value of this saving we have recourse to the Fuel Cost Chart (Fig 6, p 54), which gives the price of fuel per useful therm. Suppose the price per useful therm is 20p. Then the annual money saved by the proposed insulation of the wall will be 94 × 20p, which is £18.80.

We now have the saving in fuel cost. What about the cost of the insulation which leads to this saving? If we wish we may say that the insulation costs so many pounds to buy and fit and that it will pay for itself in so many years. For instance, suppose that the fibreboard considered above costs £100 to put in, including the cost of redecorating. Then, with a fuel saving of £18.80 per annum, it is easy to see that the insulation pays for itself in 100/18.80 years, that is in under six years.

However, we may adopt a more sophisticated approach, on the grounds that capital spent on insulation is no longer available for investment, and that our calculations should take account of the interest that is thereby forgone. We need to compare the effect of spending money now to make future fuel savings, with what we could get by leaving the capital where it is and meeting the fuel bills in full.

The comparison is made by converting the present capital cost of the insulation into an equivalent annual expenditure over the life of the insulation. This equivalent annual expenditure may be compared directly with the annual fuel saving. If the fuel saving is the larger of the two, the insulation is worth putting in. If not, not.

Table 14 shows the equivalent annual expenditure over a period of thirty years (the life of structural insulation) of £1 spent now. The annual equivalent cost varies with the rate of interest obtainable on investment. The rate to be chosen is that which the purchaser can command on his investments, whatever they may be — stocks and shares, a private business, or a bank account.

Table 14

Annual equivalent cost of money spent on thermal insulation

Rate of interest obtainable on investment (%)	Equivalent annual cost per £1 spent today (£)
2	0.0446
4	0.0578
6	0.0726
8	0.0889
10	0.1060
12	0.1241
14	0.1428
16	0.1619
18	0.1812
20	0.2008

The annual cost of the insulation is given by the cost per £1 from the table multiplied by the number of £s involved. For the example considered earlier, let us suppose the house owner can get 10 per cent interest on his investments. From Table 14 the annual equivalent cost for this rate of interest is £0.1060 per £1. So, for insulation costing £100, the annual cost will be £100 × 0.1060, that is £10.60. The fuel saving worked out at £18.80. So the overall effect of putting in the insulation is to save £8.20 net each year — the difference between the annual saving and the annual cost.

If the annual cost of the insulation works out at a higher figure than the fuel saving, then clearly it will not pay to put in the insulation. This might be the case where the structure is already thermally good. In general, however, it will be found that thermal insulation is a sound investment.

In dealing with the nett saving which can result from insulating the structure of a building, we have ignored the saving in capital cost on the heating system itself when this is put in at the same time as the thermal insulation. The reduction in size and output of boiler, pipework and heating equipment as a result of the reduced heat loss from the building can sometimes pay for the insulation outright. In such cases the annual fuel saving is pure gain and there is no annual capital charge to be deducted.

Priorities

For most British houses the biggest return will come from insulating the roof. This can most easily be done on the floor of the loft, as already described. Precautions should be taken against freezing of the water tank and pipes in the loft (see p 129) if this method is used.

Windows are probably next in priority, with walls close behind. Windows can be double glazed, and should be checked for gaps and cracks when supposedly shut. Metal frames are worse in this respect than wooden ones. Walls can be insulated in a number of ways. If one is doing the job without assistance the chief difficulty arises at window and door openings. Some ingenuity may be needed to make a neat termination to the insulated area. Some sort of framing can usually be devised.

Ventilation

Where it is possible to provide them, porches at both front and back doors are valuable heat savers. The double doors not only reduce the structural heat loss; unwanted ventilation is cut down markedly, and unnecessary air change leads to gross waste of heat. If houses were designed primarily to conserve heat — and that is why cave men came in from the cold — the control of ventilation would have a high priority. Ideally the ventilation air should be supplied to the bedrooms and ducted from there to the other rooms, being finally exhausted to outside from bathroom, lavatory and kitchen. We cannot, after all, live in every room at once, so why provide air quantities based on that assumption?

Precautions against Frost

All pipes in roof spaces or external ducts must be insulated, not only to conserve heat, but as a protection against frost. This applies to cold water pipes as well as heating pipes, and is of even greater importance when loft floor insulation is used, as the air temperature in the loft will then be much lower than before. The area beneath the cold water tank should be omitted when the loft floor is being treated, and the tank should be enclosed in a housing of strawboard or similar rigid insulation.

Chapter 11

Buying the Installation

Design, Specification and Workmanship

Once the choice of system has been made there are several possibilities open to you. If the heating is for a projected new architect-designed house the architect will certainly be willing to incorporate a heating sub-contract in the main building contract and to approach an installer for a price. However, most architects are loth to go to several firms for competitive tenders unless they have got a set of design drawings for the heating scheme and a specification. Unless your architect is willing to invite competitive tenders, this first procedure is not recommended.

If the architect expects to charge a fee on the cost of the heating installation you would do better to use the fee to employ an independent consulting engineer to design, specify and invite tenders for the installation. You should first check with your architect to see whether you will be paying him a fee on the work in any case, in addition to the consultant's fee. If so, you can either go ahead and pay the double fee or wait until the building is finished and then arrange independently for the work to be done. If a consultant is employed he must of course take full responsibility for the design.

Where no architect or consulting engineer is employed, the Heating and Ventilating Contractors' Association of Coastal Chambers, 172 Buckingham Palace Road, London SW1, will provide the names of member firms who install domestic systems. A guarantee of satisfactory workmanship can be obtained from these firms. The various fuel authorities also approve certain installers in each district, but the installations are not always formally guaranteed. When an installer's name is given by a fuel interest, the purchaser should establish whether the fuel authority or the installer is responsible for the design and workmanship of the installation. Where responsibility is apparently divided, some written acknowledgement of responsibility should always be obtained.

Installers may of course be approached by the purchaser direct. The conditions of tender — often appearing in small print on the back of the first page of the tender — should always be read with care. Any clause which appears to remove responsibility for the satisfactory design or operation of the system from the contractor should be questioned. This should be done in a letter to the contractor, and if his answer (in writing) does not clear up the point to the satisfaction of the purchaser the tender should be rejected. Several competitive prices should be obtained in any case.

Builder's Work and Electrical Wiring

The provision of a boiler plinth, the cutting of holes through brickwork for water pipes, smoke pipes etc are all builder's work. This may or may not be carried out by the heating contractor. His quotation should make quite clear what is included and what is not. If builder's work or electrical wiring work is excluded then he will be able to recommend local firms for the work and give some idea of what it should cost. In any case the heating contractor must be responsible for the provision of all information, including supplying drawings and wiring diagrams, and all the marking out on site needed for other trades' work to be carried out.

Comparing Prices and Costs

To compare prices for alternative systems we need to

131

know more than the capital cost of each installation: we need to know what each will cost to run. We also need a method of combining first cost and running cost that will let us know which is the cheaper system overall. A system which is inexpensive to buy may not be really cheap if the annual running cost is twice as much as that of the alternative. Likewise at a time of dear money — that is to say, high interest rates — money spent on a costly installation is not available for investment elsewhere, and the loss of potential interest may exceed any fuel cost savings that may be made.

There are several ways of approaching this matter. We could use the Annual Cost method, which was used in Chapter 10 to determine the savings resulting from thermal insulation. But where one of the alternatives is a method of payment by hire purchase over a comparatively short period — and such a method of payment is commonly offered for domestic heating installations — it is simpler to adopt a different approach. We shall therefore use a method based on Present Value.

Before looking into the procedure, which must, as pointed out above, take into account the annual running cost, the reader may wish to make a closer assessment of fuel cost than was derived approximately in Chapter 5. A more accurate assessment can be made from the heat loss calculations of Chapter 8. Table 15 shows the average winter heat requirement for houses with various totals of heat loss and with the two commonest programmes of use. Using the total heat loss from the calculations set out in Chapter 8, the reader may take the total winter heating requirement from the table, interpolating between the given entries as necessary. The heat needed for domestic hot water must then be added. This can be taken from Chapter 5. The total can be converted to annual fuel cost just as in Chapter 5, with the aid of the Fuel Cost Chart (Fig 6, p 54).

Table 15

Winter space heating requirements

Total house heat losses - see Chap 8 (Btu/h)	Heating system in use all day, every day, but off at night (therms)	Heating system in use morning and evening only during week, all day at weekends, but off every night (therms)
20,000	470	310
30,000	700	460
40,000	940	620
50,000	1170	770
60,000	1400	920
80,000	1870	1230
100,000	2340	1540
120,000	2800	1850
140,000	3270	2160

Present Value

Money spent on a heating installation is not available for spending elsewhere or for investment. This fact is of concern to every person who buys something as costly as a heating system, not just to those people who invest in building societies, unit trusts or stocks and shares. To pay for the installation the purchaser must do one of two things. Either he pays by drawing from his bank, savings account or other investments, where the money would continue to earn interest if it were left untouched; or he borrows the money. The borrowing may be from a bank, a private lender or from a hire purchase finance company. Paying by hire purchase is of course just one way of borrowing capital.

When money is borrowed it has to be paid back, the repayments being at the expense of future potential investment or saving; and the loan bears interest which must also be paid. The interest may be at a lower or higher rate than the purchaser can get from his savings bank or other normal investment. If a man has some form of investment that pays a high rate of interest — a business run by himself for example — he may find that he will do better to borrow the money to pay for the

133

heating installation because the interest he has to pay on the loan is at a lower rate than that he can get from investment. More commonly however the rate of interest payable on a loan is higher than most people can command on investment. Then it is cheaper to pay cash for the installation, if possible, drawing on savings or otherwise cashing investments to do so.

When there are several possible ways of paying for an installation the purchaser needs to know which is the cheapest. Some hire purchase agreements do not state the rate of interest which is charged. Unless one is familiar with discount and compound interest calculations the determination of the rate is not easy. What we shall do is reduce all the alternatives to a sum called the Present Value. The method of payment with the lowest Present Value is the cheapest. We shall find that this concept offers more than a way of comparing methods of payment. It will enable us to take all the variables into account, including running costs.

We define the Present Value (PV) of a set of future payments over a given period of time as follows. The PV is the sum of money that would need to be invested today, at an obtainable rate of compound interest, to be drawn on to meet the payments over the period in question, and to be exhausted at the end of the period. (The PV is in fact identical with the purchase price of an annuity for a fixed term of years.)

It is easy to see that if a man has to make a payment of £110 in one year's time, and he normally gets 10 per cent interest on his savings, the amount of money he must put aside today to meet the future payment is £100. The PV to him of the future £110 is therefore £100. If he could get 20 per cent interest he would need to put aside only £91.67. For that rate of interest £91.67 is the PV of the future £110. The PV depends on the rate of interest he can get.

Suppose he gets 10 per cent interest, but has to make payments of £110 for two years running. What is the PV of those payments? It will not be £200. Whatever he puts aside will bear interest at 10 per cent for the first year, the interest being added to the principal at the end of that time, when the first payment for £110 falls due. That payment is made, and the reduced principal goes on to earn 10 per cent in the second year, finishing up as an amount of £110, to meet the final payment. The PV for the two payments is in fact £190.91.

The determination of PV becomes more difficult — and ultimately intractable — as the number of payments increases, unless a general formula is used. The derivation of the general formula is not difficult, and tables of the PV of £1 per annum for varying rates of interest and periods of payment are available. We could use those. However, a chart showing Present Value for any period up to twenty years (which may be taken as the useful life of a heating system) and rates of interest up to 20 per cent will be more convenient and, for our purpose, quite accurate enough. Since we can also include a suitable range of annual payments we shall be saved the calculation necessary when tables are used.

The PV Chart

Fig 21 is a chart designed to meet our needs. There are four variables to be dealt with, so it is a little more elaborate than the charts with three variables used earlier. However, it is based on the same principle. A straight line joining a point on the left-hand vertical to a point on the right-hand vertical gives the required answer on the line in the middle. The example illustrated in broken line on Fig 21 shows the procedure.

Starting at the bottom, with the repayment period (in years), we move up to the rate of interest. This is *not* the rate charged on the loan, but the rate which the purchaser of the heating system can himself get on his investments. The intersection of the repayment period and the rate of interest gives the level of the required point on the left-hand vertical line. From that point a straight line across the chart to the annual payment on the right-hand side will cut the middle line at the PV for the total payments.

135

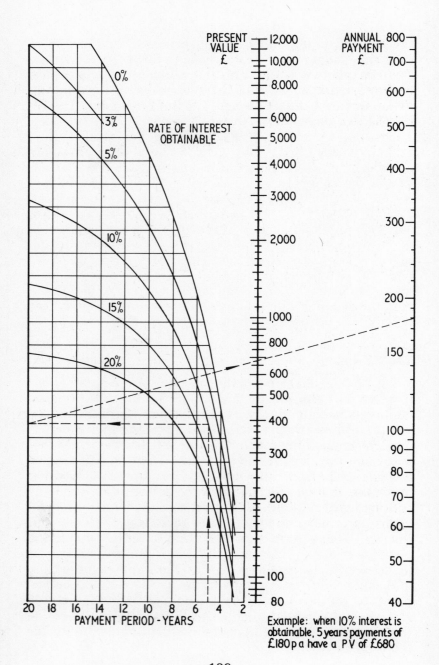

PRESENT VALUE £

ANNUAL PAYMENT £

RATE OF INTEREST OBTAINABLE

0%
3%
5%
10%
15%
20%

PAYMENT PERIOD - YEARS

Example: when 10% interest is obtainable, 5 years' payments of £180 p a have a PV of £680

Example 1

A man can get 10 per cent per annum interest on his savings in a building society. He buys a heating system on hire purchase. The agreement is for payment over five years, the annual amount being £180. What is the PV of the payments?

This is the example illustrated on the chart. From the intersection of the five-year payment-period line and the 10 per cent interest curve, move across horizontally to the left-hand vertical line. From this point a straight-edge laid across the chart to the annual payment of £180 on the right-hand vertical cuts the middle line at the point for £680. That is the PV of the total payments.

Note that the rate of interest charged by the hire purchase company does not need to be known. It is included in the amount of the annual repayments.

Example 2

The cash price for the installation in Example 1 is £600. If the purchaser pays cash, by withdrawing money from the building society to finance the project, what is the PV of the payment?

If we look at the definition of Present Value we see that for a payment made today the payment period has no length at all, so the hypothetical interest over the period is nil, and the PV is equal to the cash payment. The PV of a cash payment made now is always the amount of the payment itself. The money is, as it were, invested and then drawn out again immediately. In the case considered the PV is £600.

The purchaser in the two examples given would be wise to realise £600 of his building society investment

---

Fig 21 Present value of future expenditure   The chart provides a means of comparing the real costs of various methods of payment, including hire purchase. It also enables capital and running costs to be combined, to permit the comparison of overall costs of alternative systems

and pay the cash price. The lower PV means that it is the cheaper alternative.

Running Costs

What about running costs? Exactly the same method applies. In this case we shall not be concerned with the repayment of a loan. The running cost has to be met every year, however, and as the definition of Present Value is applicable to any recurring (or solitary) future payment, we can use it here. It reduces running costs to the same basis as capital cost and allows us to treat the two together to find the cheapest of several possible alternatives.

The PV, as we have seen, depends partly on the length of the period of payments, so we have to decide on a suitable period for the running costs. That is not difficult. The appropriate period is the useful life of the heating system. At the end of the useful life, when the installation is assumed to need replacement, the capital cost has to be met again or an alternative system paid for, and the calculations are done afresh. That is the point of time when the slate is wiped clean, as it were, and that is the point to which our running costs must be carried. The useful life of a domestic heating system may be taken as twenty years. For the determination of the *running cost* PV we therefore always use a twenty-year payment period.

The reader may welcome a word of explanation at this point. The PV, as we have seen, is a purely hypothetical sum of money: the sum which would need to be invested today to produce the required future payments if they were to be made from an invested source. The payments will in all probability be made from earned income, but the income used to make the payments is then not available for investment, and the effect is precisely as if the hypothetical course had been followed — including the effect on compound interest of the time delay between payments. The great value of the PV method is that it reduces all price alternatives and all possible methods of payment to one common basis — a basis which allows immediate comparison of costs.

Before looking at some further examples we repeat the important rule stated above. When the PV of *running cost* is required, we must use a twenty-year payment period. The period for the PV of the *capital cost* will be the loan repayment period, as in the earlier examples.

Example 3
The annual running cost of a heating system is £120. The owner can get a return of 5 per cent on his savings. What is the PV of the system running cost?

On the PV chart we find the 5 per cent interest point on the twenty-year payment line (this is the left-hand vertical itself) and put a straight-edge across the chart to an annual payment of £120. From the centre line we read off the PV as almost £1,500, say £1,495.

Example 4
The purchaser of a heating installation pays for it with the aid of a bank loan. The loan is over three years and the repayments (capital plus interest) are £240 per annum. The running cost of the system is £90 a year. If the owner can get a return on investment of 7½ per cent, what is the total PV of capital and running costs for the installation?

Capital cost: On the three-year payment-period line of the PV chart we strike a point halfway between the 5 per cent and 10 per cent interest curves — to represent 7½ per cent — and move across to the left-hand vertical. A straight line from there to an annual payment of £240 cuts the middle line at a PV of £625.

Running cost: On the twenty-year line (the left-hand vertical) find the point for 7½ per cent. Joining this to the annual payment of £90, the PV is found as £920.

Total PV, capital and running costs: £625 + £920 = £1,545.

Example 5
Would the owner of the system in Example 4 have done better if he had paid the cash price of £600 for the installation?

If he had done so the PV of the capital cost would have been £600, as explained in the solution of Example 2. (The PV of a payment made today is the amount of that payment.) The PV of £600 is less than the £625 of the bank loan repayments so, as the running cost is unaffected by this alternative, he would have done better to pay cash.

Example 6
What is the PV of the payments under a hire purchase agreement which calls for a down payment of £100 and ten annual payments of £50? The purchaser can get interest at 5 per cent on his savings.

The down payment is a payment now, and so, for the reason given in the solutions to Examples 2 and 5, it has a PV equal to itself, namely £100. The PV of the remaining payments is found from the PV chart in the usual way. It is £385. The total PV is therefore £100 + £385 = £485.

Example 7
A man receives two quotations for central heating. They are for different types of system, but equally acceptable. Whichever he finally chooses he intends to buy on hire purchase arranged by the heating installer. The first scheme would be paid for over five years at £15 per month. The running cost he estimates at £100 per annum, including maintenance. The second scheme would be paid for over five years at £10 per month, and the running cost works out at £140 per annum. The purchaser can get a return on investment of 10 per cent. Which scheme should he choose?

We take each scheme in turn and find the total PV of

purchase and running costs. We then compare the totals.

Scheme A:

Hire purchase payments: From the PV chart, using the data of 10 per cent interest and five-year period, we find the PV of the payments of £180 per annum to be £680.

Running costs: From the chart, using 10 per cent interest and a life of twenty years, the annual cost of £100 has a PV of £850.

The total PV for Scheme A is therefore £680 + £850 = £1,530.

Scheme B:

Hire purchase payments: Using 10 per cent interest and five years, we find the PV of the payments of £120 per annum to be £455.

Running costs: Using 10 per cent interest and twenty-year life, the annual cost of £140 has a PV of £1,190.

The total for Scheme B is therefore £455 + £1,190 = £1,645.

Scheme A is the cheaper of the two and should be chosen. Note that the initial outgoings are £280 for Scheme A and only £260 for Scheme B.

Using a chart to read any set of values, one is to some extent approximating. Normal eyesight will not give readings correct to more than three significant figures, if as much. The Present Values in the preceding examples are correct to this degree of accuracy. By using Present Value tables and carrying out the necessary long multiplication sums a greater numerical accuracy could be achieved. The improvement would, however, be largely spurious. The interest rate used must be to some extent conjectural. Rates change, as we all know; and the price of fuel changes with time.

Does that mean that the comparison of costs over a period is futile? It does not. When the period is short the accuracy of prediction is of course greater than when it is long. But most costs move in parallel, so a comparison may still be valid even when its components have changed with time. What can be said with confidence is that an informed choice is better than a guess. The method of comparing costs set out in this chapter allows such a choice to be made.

Index

Page numbers in bold type refer to illustrations and charts

Air, convection of, 9
Air ducts, 74-5, 106-10; flow rate, **107**; heat loss from, 106; size of, **108**
Air gaps, 121-2
Air grilles, 37, 74, **108**
Air infiltration, 48
Air locking, 69, 70
Air noise, 73-4; speed in ducts, 74
Air vents, 67, 69, 70
Annual cost, 46-57, 127-8, 132, 138-9
Annual heat requirement, 48, 50-3, 133
Approved installers, 45, 131
Automatic controls, 43, 76-87; by outdoor temperature, 43, 79-86, **87**

Back boilers, 26, 39
Balanced flue, 31, 74
Block storage heaters, 41; controlled output, 41-2
Boiler bases, 33-4
Boiler margin, 89-90, 104, 105; availability, 110-12
Boiler rating, 104-5
Boilers, 13, 14, 25-33; balanced flue, 31; convertible, 25; gas fired, 29-30; HWS, 14; magazine, 27; oil fired, 28-9; solid fuel, 25, 26-7
Boiler smoke pipe, 32, 60
British thermal unit (Btu), 8
Builder's work, 75, 131

Building Regulations, 31, 32, 34
Burner controls, 76-7
Bye-laws, 31, 34, 62

Calorific value, 30
Capacity, central plant, 110-13
Capital cost, 117
Ceiling heating, 23-4, 44, 72
Centigrade/Fahrenheit conversion, 114
Central heating, definition, 7
Chimney liners, 32
Chimneys, 30-1, 32
Circulators, *see* Pumps
Coal gas, 30
Cold feed pipe, 16, 64, 65
Conduction of heat, 48, 91, 116, 118-21
Contractor's quotation, 5, 88, 100
Controls, *see* Automatic controls
Convection: of air, 9; forced, 11; of water, 13, 14
Convectors, 21-2, 40, 70
Copper pipes, 12, 68
Corrosion, 12, 21, 73; inhibitors, 73
Cost of heat, **54**

Damp, rising, 123
Design responsibility, 58, 130-1
Design temperature, 90
Dew point, 122-3
Domestic hot water, 19-20; heating of, 12, 85, 105; system, **20**;

temperature control, 82-3; 84; *see also* Hot water cylinder
Double glazing, 119, 121-2
Drain cocks, 60, 62, 69
Draught: diverters, 32, 60; stabilisers, 32-3, 60
Drawings, 131
Ducts, *see* Air ducts

Economisers, 26
Efficiency, fuel burning, 47-8, 56
Electric heaters: block storage, 41-2; ceiling, 44-5; convectors, 40; panels, 40; radiators, 40; underfloor, 42-4, 73, 113; water heaters, 34-5
Electric heating, 34-5, 39-45; costs, 55-7; direct, 115
Electricity, heat equivalent of, 114
Electric wiring, 43, 131
Expansion: of pipes, 68-9; of water, 16, 65

Fahrenheit/centigrade conversion, 114
Fan convectors, 22, 40, 80
Feed tanks, 15, 64-5, 66, 67, 64
Fees, professional, 130
Filters, oil, 64
Fire, precautions against, 40-1, 62, 63
Fires, coal, gas, etc, 39
Fire valves, 63, 64
Fresh air inlets, 33, 60, 74
Frost: damage, 122-3; protection, 87, 129
Fuel consumption, quarterly, 55
Fuel cost chart, 54
Fuel economy: by room temperature, 10-11, 91; by automatic controls, 77-81, 86, 87; by insulation, 117
Fuel oil, 28; storage, 29, 62-3
Fuels, heat content, 47
Fuel storage, 27, 62
Fuel tariffs, 53-4, 57

Galvanised pipes, 12
Glass, 118, 119-21
GLC terminals, 60
Gravity circulation, 13, 14, 58, 85
Grilles, air, 37, 74
Guarantees, 130-1

Heat and temperature, 7-8
Heat damage, precautions, 40-1, 43
Heat, electrical equivalent, 114
Heaters, specifying, 100-1
Heat gains, 91

Heating a room, 9-11
Heating factor tables, 50-1
Heating, radiant, etc, *see* Radiant heating, etc
Heating systems: single pipe, 15, 17, 15; two pipe, 17-18, 18
Heat loss: definition, 89; factors, 93-5; composite structures, 97-9, 98; additions to structure, 99
Heat losses, 48-50, 88-99, 100, 101; determination of, 92-3
Heat saving, 77, 116-29; factors for, 125-6; by insulation, 116-129, 124; money return, 123-8
High temperature heaters, 11, 39
Hire purchase, 132, 133
Hot water cylinder, 12, 13, 14, 61-2, 70, 82-4, 85, 105; circulation to, 14-15, 58-9, 82, 83; conversion, 62; with solid fuel, 59, 83, 84; temperature control, 82-3
HWS: heat requirement, 52, 105; *see also* Domestic hot water and Hot water cylinder

Immersion heaters, 14, 62
Indirect HWS, 12, 14
Infiltration, 48
Insulating materials, 117-19
Insulation: of boilers, 60; ceiling panels, 44; ducts, 74-5; against frost, 87; hot water cylinder, 62; panel heating, 73; pipes, 69; of structure, 97-9, 116-29, 124
Insulation, benefits of, 117; heat saved by, 123-6, 124; money return from, 123-8
Insulation priorities, 128

Margin, boiler, 89-90, 104, 105
Marking out, 131
Mean radiant temperature, 10, 24, 44, 90, 117
Microbore systems, 18
Modulated control, 76, 79-81
Moisture: in walls, 122-3; barrier, 119, 123
Motorised valves, 79, 80, 85
MRT, *see* Mean radiant temperature
Multiplication chart, 49

Natural gas, 29, 30
Noise: air, 73-4; burner, 28-9

Off-peak heating, *see* Thermal storage
Off-peak tariffs, 57
Oil, fuel, 28
Oil burners, 28-9

Oil feed pipe, 63-4
Oil filled radiators, 40
Oil filters, 64
Oil fired boilers, 28-9
Oil fired installations, 62-4
Oil storage, 29, 62-3
On-off control, 76, 77-8, 85

Panel heating, 11, 23-4, 72-3, 90-1;
  control of, 81, 82
Pipe expansion, 68-9, 70
Pipe materials, 12-13, 62
Pipes, heat emission, 100, 105
Pipework, 12, 13, 68-9
Power stations, 56
Pre-heating, 84, 89, 104-5, 110-12;
  control of, 86
Present Value (PV), 132, 133-42,
  136; definition, 134
Pressure jet burners, 28-9
Pressurised system, 18
Programmers, 85
Pump head, 16, 65-8
Pump position, 65-8, 66
Pumps, 13, 15, 16, 65-8, 85
PV chart, 135, 136

Radiant heat, 9-10
Radiant heating, 11, 42-5; see also
  Panel heating
Radiators, 20-1, 40, 69, 70-2, 101;
  heat emission, 103; heating sur-
  face, 101-4; height, 102; length,
  70-1, 102, 104; position of, 9,
  72; specifying, 101-4
Radiator shelves, 72
Radiators, oil filled, 40
Radiator supports, 70
Radiator temperature, 17, 18, 102,
  103
Response, speed of, 22, 24, 117
Rising damp, 123
Room heaters, 7, 26, 30, 38-45,
  84
Room temperatures, 90; and fuel
  economy, 10-11, 24, 84, 91
Running costs, 46-57, 91, 132,
  138-9; factors affecting, 46, 48,
  91; HWS, 52, 105

Safety controls, 77
Safety valves, 61
Shower baths, 20
Sill-line heaters, 23
Skirting heaters, 22-3
Small bore pipes, 13, 73
Smoke pipes, 32, 60
Solenoid valves, 78, 83
Soot doors, 33
Specification, 88, 100, 104, 130

Steel pipes, 13
Stoking tools, 60
Structural insulation, see Insulation
Sumps, 60-1
Surface resistances, 119-22
Surface temperature limits, 44, 72

Tank contents gauge, 63
Tanks, oil storage, 29, 62-3
Temperature and heat, 7-8
Temperature conversion, 114
Temperature gradient, 11, 24, 38,
  40, 44, 73
Tenders, competitive, 130-1
Therm: definition, 47; useful, 47-
  8, 126, 54
Thermal insulation, see Insulation
Thermal reservoir, 59, 83, 84
Thermal storage, 34-5, 37, 41-4,
  84, 35; heater rating, 113-15
Thermal transmittance, 92
Thermostatic valves, 78
Thermostats, 76, 77, 83, 86, 87
Time switches, 43, 84-6, 86
Towel rails, 52
Tubular heaters, 39

Underfloor heating, 42-4, 73, 113;
  see also Panel heating
Unit heaters, 23
Units, imperial and metric, 6, 114
Units, warm air, 37, 75, 84, 110
Useful therm, 47-8, 126; cost per,
  54

Valves, 69-70, 78
Vaporising burners, 28
Vapour pressure, 122
Vapour seal, 123
Ventilation, 48, 91; excessive, 48,
  75, 129
Vent pipes, 16, 61, 63, 65
Viscosity, oil, 28

Wall cavity insulation, 118
Wallflame burners, 28
Warm air heating, 36-8, 73-5, 84,
  106-10; air flow rate, 106-10,
  107; duct sizes, 106-10, 108
Warm air units, 37, 75, 84, 110
Waste heat, use of, 56
Water: hardness, 12; expansion,
  16, 65
Water heaters, electric, 14, 34-5,
  62
'White meter' tariff, 57, 113
Windows, 119, 120-1
Wiring, electric, 43, 131; diagrams,
  131
Workmanship, 58, 130-1